D) 615.8

AN INTRODUCTION

TO

MEDICAL PHYSICS

An Introduction

to

MEDICAL PHYSICS

EDWIN G. A. AIRD, M.Sc.

Senior Physicist, Regional Medical Physics Dept.,
Newcastle General Hospital

WILLIAM HEINEMANN MEDICAL BOOKS LTD

London

First published 1975

© Edwin G. A. Aird 1975

ISBN 0 433 00350 2

Printed in Great Britain by William Clowes & Sons Limited
London, Colchester and Beccles

Contents

FOR EILEEN

Preface

The application of physics to medicine is a relatively new and rapidly changing discipline. The number of people working in medical physics has increased enormously within the last two decades. so it seemed an appropriate time to write a book to introduce medical physics to those people unfamiliar with the subject. This book is primarily intended for technicians, radiographers and graduate or specialist nurses, but it should also be useful to the graduate scientist entering the field of medical physics.

There are now in existence a number of O.N.C. courses in medical physics. I have not attempted to follow any particular syllabus, but have written on the topics most commonly encountered by technicians and radiographers working in medical physics or nuclear medicine. There are two broad sections to the book: the first dealing with the subject of ionising radiation and its various uses, the second with various other applications of physics to medicine. I intend the chapters on radiotherapy physics, radiodiagnostic physics and radiation hazards and protection to be a useful adjunct to other texts for radiographers, as well as being of value to technicians who are also involved with these subjects. The other main chapter in the section on ionising radiation is on the use of radioisotopes in diagnosis, sometimes known as nuclear medicine. I have written in some detail on this subject as it has a rapidly expanding number of applications in all branches of medicine, and should be useful to technicians in laboratories in medical physics, nuclear medicine and pathology and to radiographers working for their special qualification in this subject.

I have attempted to contain the other subjects in separate chapters and to give an understanding of the physics involved in each subject without writing a book on physiology or electronics. The use of ultrasonics in diagnosis is a large and expanding subject with many interesting applications but I have confined myself only to the essentials of this subject. Physiological measurement is an important field of work and I thought it worthwhile to describe some of the basic techniques involved.

A relatively new subject for the medical physicist is audiology and I have described the basics of this interesting subject. Computing is essential in every scientific field, so in the final chapter I have given an introduction to this subject as well as describing some of its applications to medicine.

This book covers a large field of work so necessarily the content is mainly descriptive. For the reader who wishes to study a particular subject in depth I have listed some of the excellent works available (see Books Consulted p. 284) in the individual subjects.

I am grateful to Professor F. T. Farmer and Dr. M. J. Day for their advice and encouragement and to the staff of the medical physics department at Newcastle General Hospital for their advice and some of the illustrations. For many of the line drawings I would like to thank the University Department of Photography. For photographs of equipment I am grateful to:

Philips Medical Systems Limited
J. and P. Engineering (Reading) Limited
Nuclear Enterprises Limited
I.C.N. Tracerlab (U.K.) Limited
SIEMENS

CHAPTER 1

Introduction

A standard definition of medicine is the art or science of the prevention and cure of disease; physics is defined as natural philosophy, the science of properties of matter and energy. In the latter part of the eighteenth century men of medicine were making very significant contributions to physics: Galvani and Volta, who were among the leading scientists of the time were in fact physiologists, Young and Poiseuille were physicians. Thus until the middle of the nineteenth century it was physicians who were contributing to physical science, but from this time physics expanded rapidly in association with the technical advances of the industrial revolution. Now medicine and physics are very separate disciplines even though medicine has become much more scientifically based; physics as a pure subject is now concerned with abstract theories concerning such esoteric subjects as the "strangeness" of nuclear particles. In medical physics the two subjects are not combined to produce a subject in itself, physics is applied to medicine to improve its techniques and to develop new techniques. The term medical physics is simply convenient for use within the hospital environment. The physicist working in medicine brings to it his basic knowledge of how things work: the properties of radiation, the theories of fluid flow, measurement of pressure, the electrical properties of body tissues, the applications of logic to dynamic systems, and the use of the computer. This knowledge and its careful application allow the physicist, in collaboration with his medical colleagues and, if necessary, other scientists within the hospital, to provide a very valuable research and development service as well as a routine service.

Even though it is difficult to define the subject medical physics, several topics have developed from medical physics departments into self-contained subjects, e.g. radiation dosimetry, image processing, radioisotope diagnosis, ultrasonic diagnosis, and cardiological physics. Many of these subjects are now essential to a large hospital and can exist either within a

1

medical physics department, or as separate branches within the hospital served by a physics department. To understand the structure and place of medical physics more fully, especially in the U.K., it is necessary to look at the historical background.

Surprisingly it was the pure physicist working in the field of ionising radiation who first supplied a valuable contribution to medicine in recent history. The discovery of radium followed closely by the discovery of X-rays led immediately to the rapid development of radio-therapy and radiodiagnosis. The physicist became involved in determining the properties of these radiations and the measurement of their intensity. At first he was remote from the hospital environment, but when the hazards of the use of these radiations became apparent the physicist soon found himself involved directly with medical staff and with patients. The first appointment in medical radiation physics was made in 1910 in Britain. At this time developments in radiation measurement by ionisation methods were being made, particularly in Britain. The contribution of physics to the various aspects of radiology at this time is illustrated by the fact that at the 1st International Congress of Radiology in London (1924) physics occupied sufficient time to fill a subsequent complete edition of the *British Journal of Radiology*. The rapid improvement of X-ray tubes and generators provided more penetrating beams of radiation; both this and the increasing use of radium kept the physicist busy improving accuracy of measurement and producing distributions of radiation dose within the body.

Meanwhile rapid developments were taking place in nuclear physics. In 1911 Rutherford proposed an atomic theory (based on alpha-particle scattering experiments) including the new concept of a positively charged concentration of matter at the centre of the atom with the negative charge spread over a sphere of radius similar to the radius of the atom. Between 1913 and 1915 Bohr, a Danish physicist, developed a theory of the atom with a central nucleus and electrons moving in different orbits, to account for the properties of atomic spectra. The first artificial nuclear disintegration was produced by Rutherford in 1919 by bombarding nitrogen atoms with alpha particles; which was accompanied by the emission of protons. The neutron was proposed by Rutherford in 1920 to account for the failure of the proton-electron hypothesis of the nucleus in accounting for certain properties of the atom. Because of its neutral charge, many unsuccessful attempts were made to detect the presence of the neutron; it was not until 1932 that Chadwick at Cambridge demonstrated its existence. On the theoretical side of nuclear physics Planck and Einstein developed the quantum theory of radiation to explain phenomena which could not be explained fully by classical theory. The culmination of all this work came in the form of one of the most outstanding events of scientific history: the enormous energy released when a quantity of material is fissioned. The war years brought frantic effort from some of the nations involved to be the first to produce the massive chain reaction in which the fission energy from a mass of uranium is almost simultaneously released, and which would be dramatic proof of Einstein's equation $E = mc^2$. The U.S.A. won the race to the cost of thousands of lives in Japan from the dropping of the atomic bombs on Hiroshima and Nagasaki. The irony of this horrifying event is that, not only had the concentration of resources and time been spent which laid the way for the production of many isotopes useful to medicine and biology, but the conscience of many workers in the atomic weapons field caused them to turn to the medical field for their further career as atonement.

The really rapid expansion of medical physics has been relatively recent, since 1950. Cobalt-60 became available in large enough quantities for deep external beam radiotherapy; iodine-131 was used for both therapeutic and diagnostic purposes; and the linear accelerator underwent development to make it suitable for routine clinical use. The first linear accelerator was installed in Hammersmith in 1953 followed closely by Newcastle General Hospital, St. Bartholomew's Hospital and The Christie Hospital, Manchester. The design of these machines was very largely a result of the war effort through the development of high power magnetrons for radar.

It was becoming increasingly apparent at this time that efficient radiation detection equipment was needed, especially to measure small quantities of radioactivity in the body. The Geiger-Muller tube was invented in 1929, but the first commercial tube was not available until 1947, manufactured by Twentieth Century Electronics. Scintillation crystals and the photomultiplier tubes necessary to detect the scintillations produced in these crystals by radiation, became available in the 1950s. These provided great improvement in detection efficiency of gamma rays. The ancillary counting equipment was developed at about the same time; bulky valve equipment was later replaced by transistors which had faster switching times and could deal with high counting rates. In the mid-1960s integrated circuits became available for use in counting equipment, they were especially valuable in the switching logic of the scaler itself.

To visualise the distribution of activity within the body a scanning system is necessary. The first automatic scanner was produced in 1956 which displayed the scan as photodots on film; colour display was introduced in 1959 and the first commercially available scanner was installed in the U.K. in 1960. At the same time, in the U.S., Anger was developing what he called a gamma camera; a system using a large scintillation crystal for imaging a complete organ of the body containing radio-isotope on to a single picture. From 1960 rapid advances in technique were made with the implementation of new equipment in radio-isotope work. More physicists were appointed to deal with the various aspects of the use of radio-isotopes in medicine. These appointments were mostly in departments where there already existed a physics service to radiotherapy, but there were some to radio-isotope departments which were starting up on their own. Some of the physicists' tasks within a radio-isotope department were as follows: (i) the storage, handling and disposal of radio-isotopes and the minimising of the radiation contamination hazards during these operations, (ii) the accurate dispensing of radio-isotopes, (iii) the setting of detection systems for their most efficient use, (iv) the design of collimators for efficient detection of radiation from the body, (v) the day-to-day running of this equipment, (vi) the introduction of image processing with the use of a computer.

By 1970 many radio-isotope techniques were well established and ready to take their place among the wide range of tests available within the large general hospital. For example, many of the *in vitro* tests using radio-active materials to label reagents could be done in pathology departments; so these departments acquired their own counting equipment and already have the staff available to deal with the large growth of work in this field. But the physicist must still be available to set up the apparatus initially and to check the working of the system from time to time as well as to act as radiation protection adviser.

Throughout the period 1920-1960 medical physics departments had become established in the main teaching hospitals in the U.K., in some cases closely linked with universities. With its roots in radiation physics medical physics in these departments was concerned with dosimetry in radiotherapy, radio-isotope work and some diagnostic X-ray work as well as general radiation protection. However, other subjects were also investigated by medical physicists. If a medical man was interested in a particular subject he could discuss it with a physicist, who would use his knowledge of physics and electronics to develop the topic further than simply producing a solution to the original problem.

One subject which is now established within hospitals as a valuable diagnostic aid is ultrasonic imaging. This subject has a strange history, as although the phenomenon was well-known—and the theories of propagation of ultrasound were well established by the beginning of the twentieth century—it needed the development of modern electronics to allow ultrasound to be developed as a diagnostic tool. The First World War saw the first use of high-frequency ultrasound power in the detection of submarines. The Second World War produced further developments especially in fast electronic pulse techniques. Pulse echo-detection equipment then became available for use in the industrial field to detect flaws in metal. This type of equipment was used medically in the 1950s to determine mid-line displacement within the brain; the first two-dimensional scanners were developed at about the same time. After a late start ultrasound diagnosis expanded rapidly after 1960, to become an accepted diagnostic aid in gynaecology, neurology, and to a lesser extent in urology and other disciplines.

Cardiology has also demanded the application of physics: in improving measuring devices and electronic systems for measuring electrical activity within the heart and for measuring pressures in the heart. Computer analysis has improved the accuracy of diagnosis from these signals. Use of the computer in automatically determining irregularity in heart beat has become essential in busy intensive care units. In all these subjects the physicist provides a service as well as developing new techniques.

The Present Status of Medical Physics
It is difficult to define precisely the physicist's role within the hospital. The Zuckerman Report[1] places the physicist in a

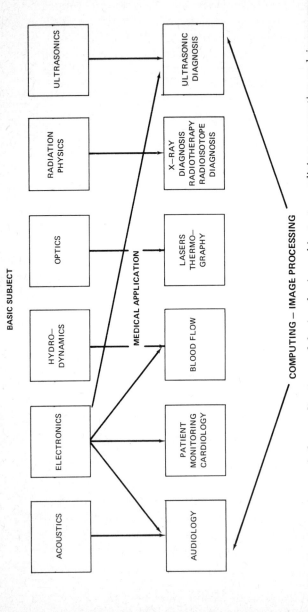

Fig. 1.1. To show some of the applications of basic physics subjects to medicine; computing and image processing embraces the whole range of subjects.

group of non-medically qualified graduate scientists including: biochemists, physicists, clinical psychologists and other scientists, and defines the work of the physicist by the statement: "(physicists) conduct physical measurements in the field of radiation physics, diagnostic and therapeutic use of radio-isotopes, and medical electronics and instrumentation, and may have teaching and training commitments. In addition they carry out research and development on medical equipment and on physical problems arising in a wide range of clinical specialities". Similarly since it varies from hospital to hospital, it is difficult to define a typical medical physics department structure. A relatively large department may contain 15-20 graduate physicists and 40-50 technical staff. As defined by the Zuckerman Report, medical physics technicians: "provide technical assistance to physicists and doctors who are concerned with the application of physics and nuclear physics to medicine ... duties may include the construction, maintenance and operation of electronic and mechanical apparatus used in the diagnosis and treatment of patients—including that depending on the use of radiation and radio-isotopes—the construction and operation of patient monitoring equipment, and the application of computer and display techniques". In a department of this size the following subjects would be typical:

Radiotherapy physics*
{
Dosimetry
Development of the use of the computer
Machine fault finding and some maintenance
}

Radio-isotopes*
{
Initial settings on instruments
Image processing
Research and development of particular tests
}

Medical electronics and instrumentation
X-ray diagnosis*
Ultrasonics
Cardiological physics and patient monitoring
Bloodflow measurement

* The physicist is involved in radiation protection in these subjects.

[1] Hospital Scientific and Technical Sources, Report of Committee chaired by Sir Solly Zuckerman (1965).

Audiology
Data analysis and signal processing
Use of the computer in general.

Other subjects which the physics department might become involved with in the relatively short-term are:

Thermography
Physical medicine
Telemetry

Thus we see that medical physics is an applied science; it is physics especially directed at medicine and the research work done is essentially applied rather than basic. The function of the physicist in these roles is necessarily complex; he must collaborate with clinicians in the physical interpretation of results, but he must neither get too involved with the precision of one parameter that he ignores the rest, nor must he try to encompass so many disciplines that he becomes dilettante. Collaboration is essential since the physicist and the physician approach a problem in different ways; the physicist looking at the particular, the clinician fitting the information from various measurements to what he sees and hears from the patient himself.

CHAPTER 2

Basic Physics

In any book on physics or the use of physics there is continual reference to energy, pressure, force, etc.—very common concepts to the physicist—and it is essential for anyone reading a book of this nature to have a full understanding of the meaning of these terms.

Energy. At the very basis of all physical phenomena is the concept of energy in its various forms and that it can neither be created nor destroyed; if it disappears in one form it always reappears in some other form. It is this fundamental law which has aided physicists in many discoveries especially in the field of nuclear physics. A simple definition of energy is that it is *stored work* and it is measured in Joules.

Work. Work is done when a force moves the point on which it acts.

Force. This is the agency which is capable of changing the state of rest of a body or its uniform motion. It is particularly easy to see how forces act in mechanics; all action is determined according to Newton's laws: (1) Every body remains in its state of rest, or of uniform motion in a straight line unless a force acts upon it. (2) The rate at which a body changes its momentum is proportional to the applied force and takes place in the direction of a straight line along which the force acts. This can be expressed by the equation:

$$F = \frac{d(mv)}{dt};$$

where m is mass of body and v is its velocity. (3) To every action there is an equal and opposite reaction.

Intensity. This is the flux of energy per unit area or the energy flux density.

Power. This is the rate at which work is done, and is measured in Joules/sec or watts.

It is useful at this point to see how these terms are used in some different branches of physics.

9

Mechanics. This is particularly concerned with potential and kinetic energy and the forces which change the energy of a body. They can be illustrated by the following sequence of events: If a ball is thrown vertically upwards it is given an initial velocity depending on the force with which it was thrown. Gravitational force now acts on the ball to oppose its motion; the ball works against this force so using up kinetic energy until it comes to rest. However, the energy is not lost, it has been transformed into potential energy due to the ball's height and equal to mgh; where m = mass of ball, g = gravitational constant, h = height above ground.

As the ball now falls to earth again it loses potential energy and gains kinetic energy; if there is no friction to slow it down, it reaches the ground at the same velocity at which it was projected, and with a kinetic energy equal to $\frac{1}{2}mv^2$. If the kinetic energy is equated to the potential energy the velocity can be expressed as $v^2 = 2gh$, i.e. the velocity is independent of the mass of the falling object. Within these arguments there is only a single object involved, so the term intensity is not relevant.

Ionising radiation. However, when large numbers of identical particles are considered, e.g. photons, intensity is a necessary parameter to describe the photon flux. The energy of each photon is given from quantum theory as $E = h\nu$; where h is Planck's constant, and ν is the frequency of the radiation. If there are N photons per second passing through an area the intensity is given by:

$$N \cdot h\nu \text{ per unit area per second.}$$

The unit of intensity is thus: joules $\cdot$ metre^{-2} $\cdot$ second^{-1}.

In radiotherapy it is necessary to find the *absorbed dose*; this is the energy absorbed per unit volume by a body and would have units $J \cdot kg^{-1}$. The special unit of absorbed dose is the rad = 1/100 J/kg.

The absorbed dose rate can be found from the intensity I of the beam of radiation if the mass energy absorption coefficient is known using the formula:

Absorbed dose rate = $I \cdot$ (mass energy absorption coefficient)

$$\text{with units } J \cdot m^{-2} \cdot s^{-1} \cdot m^2 \cdot kg^{-1}.$$

Matter waves. These are caused by oscillations at the various frequencies within the infra-, normal, and ultrasound ranges.

When describing these waves it is the amplitude of the oscillation which is of interest, since the intensity of the matter wave is given by:

$$I = (\text{amplitude})^2, \text{ in units of watt/metre}^2.$$

It is often necessary to know the total power of matter waves; this is given from: Power $= I \times$ (area over which the intensity acts).

The power ratio is a useful parameter when measuring the absorption or reflection of sound or ultrasound beams. Since the changes in power or intensity can be of several magnitudes a logarithmic ratio is used:

$$\text{Power ratio} \quad = \log_{10} \frac{P_1}{P_2} \text{ bel;} \quad \text{or } 10 \log_{10} \frac{P_1}{P_2} \text{ decibel.}$$

$$\text{Intensity ratio} = \log_{10} \frac{I_1}{I_2} \text{ bel;} \quad \text{or } 10 \log_{10} \frac{I_1}{I_2} \text{ decibel.}$$

Where the suffixes 1 and 2 refer to the respective power or intensity levels. There is another relation which is useful. Since the intensity is proportional to the mean square pressure exerted on an area at right angles to the given direction; the pressure ratio is given by:

$$20 \log_{10} \frac{p_1}{p_2} \text{ dB.}$$

Electricity. The simplest example of work being done in electricity is when current, I, flows through a resistance causing its temperature to rise. If the voltage across the resistance is V, the work done in the resistance is $P = IV$, or $P = I^2 R$. This is actually a rate of working as can be seen if the equation is written $P = (QV)/t$ where Q is the quantity of charge moved through the potential difference in time, t, and QV is the amount of work necessary to do it.

If Q is in coulombs, V is in volts, and P in watts, the work is expressed in terms of joules. Unless the flow of electrons is considered on the atomic scale, as in solid state physics, it is not usual to use the term intensity in electricity; it is the power, IV, which is of interest. When considering the performance of electrical systems such as amplifiers-it is power ratios which are of interest.

In the X-ray tube electrons are accelerated through a high

potential, V, so acquiring an energy of $E = eV$, since the charge on an electron is equal to e coulombs (1.6×10^{-19} coulombs). This energy is so small that it is given the name electron-volt, 1 electron volt equals 1.6×10^{-19} joules. It is usual to describe the energies of ionising radiations in terms of kilo electron-volts, 1keV = 1.6×10^{-16} J and megaelectron-volts, 1MeV = 1.6×10^{-13} J.

SI units. Recently there has been an attempt to simplify and standardise the many systems of units that are used by introducing the Système International d'Unités which is intended to be used universally. This system of units was the outcome of a resolution of the Ninth General Conference of Weights and Measures in 1948, which instructed an international committee to study the establishment of a complete set of rules for units of measurement.

The SI system contains three classes of units: (i) base, (ii) derived, (iii) supplementary. The base units are the following: metre, kilogramme, second, ampere, kelvin, candela and mole. Derived units can be formed from combinations of base units, e.g. the unit of force is a combination of kilogramme, metres and seconds, and has been given the name of newton, 1 newton = 1 kilogramme . metre . second^{-2}. The basic supplementary units are the radian and steradian, but other units are still in use in particular specialities. At the time of writing a decision has not yet firmly been made concerning the basic radiation units: the rad. the roentgen and the curie.

RADIATION

Radiation is the propagation of energy. If an object or instrument emits energy in any form then it is said to be emitting radiation. An example of radiant energy which is very familiar is that of matter waves in the form of sound radiation. If a tuning fork is struck the noise it makes is heard almost immediately by an observer standing nearby. The oscillations of the fork cause vibrations to be started that alternately compress and expand small volumes of air in the immediate vicinity of the fork. As there is nothing to prevent it this energy in the form of a pressure wave travels out from its source. When the wave reaches the human ear it sets up vibrations of the eardrum by transferred energy; this is the "noise" which is heard when these vibrations are transduced to the brain. At a long distance from a source of noise it is possible to notice a definite time lag between seeing the fork struck and hearing the sound. Sound radiation is thus the propagation of energy in the form of compressions and rarefactions of the medium (see fig. 2-1) through which it travels at a definite speed. In medical physics the physics of sound waves are important in audiology; in the ultrasonic frequency range the properties of these waves are studied because of their importance in the diagnostic field.

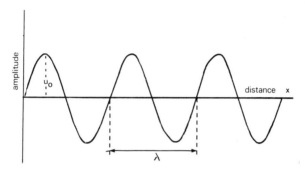

Fig. 2.1. A wave motion. The relationship of wavelength (λ) to frequency (v) is λ = v/v, where v is velocity of wave.

Electromagnetic radiation. Sound waves consist of changes within a medium; small sections of the medium oscillate as the energy wave passes, there is no movement of particles in the direction of energy propagation. The other important group of radiations, which come under the heading of electromagnetic radiation, propagates energy in the form of various particles of travelling electric or magnetic fields, thus needing no medium through which to travel. The most familiar of these are radio waves which are energy waves transmitted from an aerial and travel at very high speeds (186,000 miles per second, or 3×10^8 metres per second) to be received virtually instantaneously within the normal broadcasting distances. Delay between transmission and reception can be noticed over the distances reached by astronauts, e.g. radio signals from the moon, which is at a distance of approximately a quarter of a million miles, take just over a second to reach the earth.

Light waves are also members of the electromagnetic spectrum and have the same very high speed of propagation, which has become incorporated in the astronomical unit of 1 light year, i.e. the distance that light travels in one year. Both light and radio radiations can be analysed in terms of changing electric and magnetic waves. However, certain phenomena associated with light can only be explained by regarding the energy as transported by discrete bundles of energy known as photons. One of the first phenomena which could only be explained by this quantisation was the photoelectric effect, in which it was found that the energy of an electron escaping from a photocathode did not depend on the intensity of the light falling on the photoelectric surface, but did depend on the colour of the light.

In the wave theory of radiation the wavelength, λ, and frequency ν of the wave are related by the formula $c = \lambda\nu$; where c is the velocity of propagation. For example, radio waves have wavelengths of typically 300 metres; light waves have much shorter wavelengths:

infrared   12,000 Å
visible   6,000 Å
ultraviolet 3,000 Å (1 Å = 10^{-10} metres).

The colour of light thus depends on wavelength or frequency. A quantum of light, a photon, is an energy packet with an energy $E = h\nu$; where h is Planck's constant = 6.62×10^{-34} joules · second.

In terms of wavelength $E = 12.4/\lambda$ electron volts. Visible light photons thus have energies of about 2 eV; infra-red (n.b. thermal radiation) photons have energies of about 1 eV. Ultraviolet photons can have energies up to several tens of electron volts; these hard ultraviolet radiations can produce ionisation in the same way as very low-energy X-rays (10 kiloelectron volts).

Ionising radiation. At higher energies there are the hard X-rays used in high energy X-ray radiotherapy (with energies up to thirty million electron volts) and gamma rays from radio isotopes which are used in both radiotherapy and radio diagnosis (with energies up to several million electron volts). To explain certain phenomena, e.g. X-ray diffraction, it is still necessary to regard X-rays as electromagnetic waves, however, many effects can only be explained using quantum theory, i.e. regarding the energy propagation in terms of photon flux.

Other radiations. X- and gamma radiations are sometimes described in terms of beams of particles to describe certain phenomena. Certain beams of particles also come under the general heading of ionising radiation: beta particles and alpha particles are examples of interest in medicine. These interact with matter in a different manner to that described below, and are absorbed very quickly.

Attenuation of Radiation

There are two causes of a reduction in intensity of a radiation beam: (i) the inverse square law effect, (ii) the absorption of radiation by the medium through which it travels.

Inverse square law. If a source is emitting radiation in all directions there is the same flux, F, over the surface of any sphere centred on the source. If one sphere has a radius, r_1, and the second a radius, r_2, the surface areas of these spheres are respectively $4\pi r_1^2$ and $4\pi r_2^2$, and the intensity at each surface is $I_1 = F/4\pi r_1^2$ and $I_2 = F/4\pi r_2^2$. The ratio of the intensities is then $I_1/I_2 = (r_2/r_1)^2$, i.e. intensity is inversely proportional to the square of the distance from the source.

Absorption of radiation. The absorption of electromagnetic radiation and in particular the absorption of X- and gamma-ray photons will be discussed here, as the absorption of ultrasonic radiation is discussed in the chapter on the use of ultrasonics in medical diagnosis. Absorption of beta radiation is discussed in the chapter on radiotherapy. The beta particle gives up a definite amount of energy at each interaction with an atom or molecule producing ionisation or excitation. It does this repeatedly as it passes through a medium until all its energy has been absorbed and it comes to rest within an atom. The absorption of X- or gamma-ray photons is distinctly different. Since they have no charge the processes of absorption are different, resulting in an element of chance that a particular photon will interact at all with the medium. Because of this probability factor a given photon may interact immediately with the medium, or it may pass right through without interaction. The number of photons removed from a beam of N photons depends directly on N. This leads to the concept of exponential absorption: if the thickness of the medium is Δt then the number of photons removed $\Delta N = -\mu N \Delta t$; where μ is the absorption coefficient. When integrated this equation becomes $N = N_0 e^{-\mu t}$ (this curve is illustrated in fig. 2-2); where N is the number of photons transmitted and N_0 is the number incident. In terms of radiation intensity $I = I_0 e^{-\mu t}$; where I is the transmitted intensity and I_0 is the incident intensity.

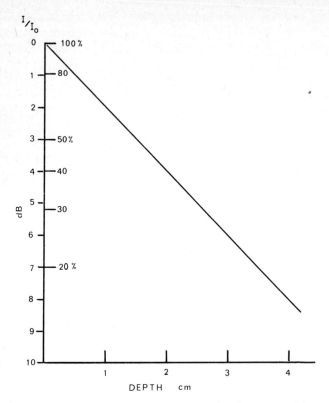

Fig. 2.2. An exponential absorption curve (log/linear graph). $\mu = 0.46$ cm^{-1}, H.V.L. = 1.5 cm.

The interaction processes. If various materials and various thicknesses of material are placed in gamma-ray beams of different energies and the absorption measured, certain factors emerge concerning the degree of absorption: (i) the higher the energy the less the absorption, (ii) low-energy beams are absorbed almost completely by high atomic number materials, (iii) for high-energy beams the same quantity of any material (in mass per unit area) absorbs the same amount of radiation. The gamma rays interact with a medium in three distinct ways depending on the energy and atomic number of the medium: (i) photoelectric effect, (ii) Compton scattering, (iii) pair production. (See fig. 2-3a, b.)

Photoelectric effect. In the standard model of the atom (see p. 27) the electrons are considered to be in various energy shells

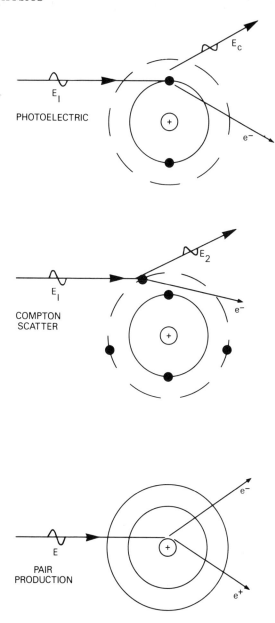

Fig. 2.3. (a) The interaction processes of photons with matter. (b) A table showing the energies of the various particles for the different processes and the chance of occurrence for different energy incident photons.

Photoelectric

Incident Photon:	E_1	E_c	Electron	Chance of Occurrence
Lead	200 keV	88 keV	112 keV	90%
	4000	88	3912	5%
Tissue	30	0.5	29.5	41%
	100	0.5	99.5	1.4%
	200	0.5	199.5	0.25%

Compton Scatter

Incident Photon:	E_1	E_2	Electron	Chance of Occurrence
Lead	200 keV	144 keV	56 keV	10%
	4000	3540	460	55%
Tissue	30	28.5	1.5	59%
	100	84	16	98.65
	200	144	56	99.75%

Pair Production

Incident Photon:	E	Electron	Positron	Chance of Occurrence
Lead	200 keV	—	—	0%
	4000	1.49 MeV	1.49 MeV	40%
Tissue	4000	1.49	1.49	5.8%

Fig. 2.3. (b)

surrounding the nucleus. If a photon with energy greater than the binding energy of an electron in, for example, the K orbit is in collision with one of these electrons, the photon disappears and its energy is transferred to the electron, removing it from its shell and giving it some kinetic energy. There is now an energy gap in the atom which must be filled. This is done very quickly by attracting an electron from one of the lower energy levels. The filling of this hole releases a definite amount of energy in the form of a characteristic X-ray photon. Because this type of absorption is achieved with the bound electrons it depends on the atomic number of the medium; in fact the amount of absorption, measured in terms of mass absorption coefficient, depends approximately on (atomic number)^3. The effect also decreases rapidly with the photon energy (approximately as $1/E^3$), thus the mass absorption coefficient, $\tau/\rho \propto (Z/E)^3$.

Compton scattering. If the photon energy is much greater than the energy of the bound electrons the photons are not completely absorbed; they bounce off the electrons like billiard balls losing some of their energy on impact to the electron, which is ejected with a certain kinetic energy. All the electrons of an atom produce the same effect on a photon because the binding energy is very small compared with the photon energy. Thus it does not matter what the atomic number of the medium is when considering the amount of scatter; only the electron density—which is very closely related to the density of the medium—is important, i.e. all materials (except hydrogen and its compounds) scatter equally by the Compton process. The amount of scatter decreases with energy, $\sigma/\rho \propto 1/E$ (approximately).

Pair production. This third process does not occur in diagnostic X-ray and is of little importance in most radiotherapy and diagnostic radioisotope work. Both the photoelectric effect and Compton scattering involve the electrons of the atom, however, if a photon has sufficient energy it can penetrate the electron shells and pass close to the nucleus. In this region of very powerful forces the photon disappears and an electron and a positron are produced which have a velocity depending on the energy of the photon. This is a clear example of the dual roles of energy and matter and illustrates Einstein's law $E = mc^2$. There is a threshold energy to this reaction as the energy of the photon must be greater than the rest masses of the electron and positron, given by the equation:

$$E = \frac{2 \times 9.1 \times 10^{-31} \times (3 \times 10^8)^2}{1.6 \times 10^{-13} \text{ (J per MeV)}} = 1.02 \text{ MeV}.$$

Absorption by this process increases with atomic number and increases with energy.

Absorption in body tissues. All the soft tissues of the body have a low effective atomic number ($\bar{Z} = 7.5$). Thus photons of energies greater than 30 keV interact predominantly by Compton scattering (see fig. 2-4). This means that there is

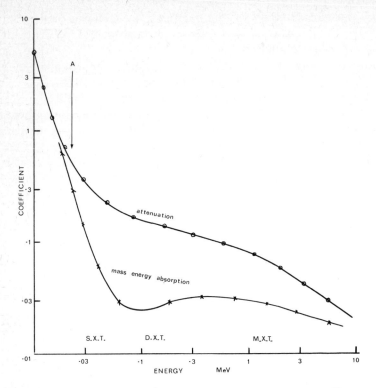

Fig. 2.4. A comparison of the mass energy absorption coefficient of water to its attenuation coefficient. At A the chance of an interaction occurring by the photoelectric effect is equal to the chance of a Compton interaction.

always an appreciable amount of scattered radiation in X-ray diagnosis and in radiotherapy, which is important when considering protection from radiation. Bone has a higher effective atomic number ($\bar{Z} = 13$) than soft tissue which means that, particularly at low energies where photoelectric effect predominates, the absorption in bone can be many times higher than in soft tissue.

Absorption coefficient. It is important to distinguish between absorption and attenuation. The amount of energy removed from the beam by a material is the absorbed energy, and it is this energy which determines the effect of the radiation on the material. The rate of removal of energy is given by: $I \cdot (\mu/\rho)_e$; where $(\mu/\rho)_e$ is the mass energy absorption coefficient for a given energy and medium and I is intensity. This absorption coefficient is determined by the amount of energy given to the secondary electron produced by the interaction of the photon with an atom. If a photon is absorbed by the photoelectric process all its energy is given up; with the Compton effect, however, the photon only gives a certain amount of energy to the electron, and the scattered photon with the remaining energy may not be absorbed by the body at all. Thus there are two parts to the absorption coefficient, a real part, which is the mass energy absorption coefficient, and a scattered part. The total absorption coefficient is the sum of the P.E., scatter and P.P. coefficients and determines the total attenuation of the primary beam (see fig. 2-4). The real part of this determines the energy absorbed.

Attenuation coefficient. When considering the effect of a medium on a beam of radiation it is the reduction in the intensity of the beam, and the attenuation coefficient that are of interest. At low energies, in media where the photoelectric effect predominates, the mass attenuation coefficient is almost equal to the mass energy absorption coefficient; at medium and high photon energies (100-4000 keV) these coefficients may differ by as much as a factor of two because of the scatter portion of the mass absorption coefficient. The units of either of these coefficients are: metre^2 per kilogram, since the thicknesses are conveniently referred to in terms of kilogram per metre^2. The equation of the attenuation of intensity becomes $I = I_0 \ e^{-\mu/\rho \, \cdot \, \rho d}$, where d is the linear thickness of the medium in metres, ρ is the density of the medium.

Linear attenuation coefficient. In protection problems it is frequently the linear dimensions of structures which are relevant, and a linear absorption coefficient is then required. This is given by: mass attenuation coefficient x density. Thus although the mass attenuation coefficients for different materials are very similar for high photon energies, their linear attenuation coefficients differ by the ratio of the densities of the materials, e.g. the linear attenuation coefficients of lead and concrete differ by about a factor of five (11.6/2.2). The unit of linear attenuation coefficient is metre^{-1}.

Half-value layer. A useful measure of attenuation is the HVL: that thickness of material which reduces the radiation intensity of a narrow beam to one-half of its value (see fig. 2-2).

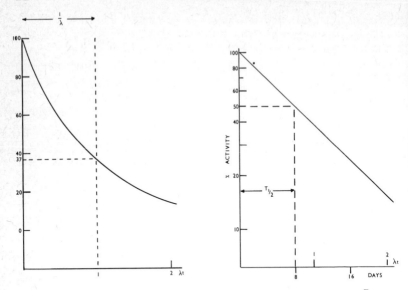

Fig. 2.5. (a) An exponential decay curve showing the mean life, $\bar{T} = 1/\lambda$. (b) An exponential curve plotted on a logarithmic scale.

Parameters Used in Connection with Radioactive Sources

Activity. This is the number of nuclei which disintegrate in a radioactive nuclide in unit time. The special unit of activity is the curie:

$$1 \text{ curie} = 3.7 \times 10^{10} \text{ disintegrations per sec.}$$

Activity is closely connected to the intensity of radiation: (i) for gamma rays by the k factor (p. 78) — exposure rate = $(k \cdot A)/d^2$ R/hr, where A = activity, and d is distance from the source. (ii) for beta rays the rate of total energy absorbed by a body containing a source of activity A emitting beta particles of mean energy $\bar{E}$, is $\bar{E} \cdot A$ or $1.6 \times 10^{13} \bar{E} \cdot A$ J/s.

Exponential decay. The exponential function can be frequently used to describe certain phenomena in nature. An exact exponential describes the decay of a pure radionuclide. This is because the rate of decay depends on the number of radioactive atoms remaining $dN/dt = \lambda N$; which integrates to give $N = N_0 e^{-\lambda t}$; where N_0 is the initial number of radioactive atoms, and λ is the decay constant.

Half-life. A useful measure of the decay of a radionuclide is its half-life: the time taken for a pure radionuclide to decay to half its initial activity. It is related to the decay constant by $T_{1/2} = 0.693/\lambda$, since $\log_e (2) = 0.693$. Thus if $T_{1/2} = 8$ days the decay constant is $0.693/8 \times 24 \times 3,600$ second^{-1} (fig. 2-5b).

Mean life. The integral of the exponential curve from zero to infinity is

$$A \int\limits_{0}^{-\infty} e^{-\lambda t} \cdot dt = \frac{A}{\lambda};$$

which is the total number of radioactive atoms which have decayed in this time. But we have already seen that $\lambda = 0.693/T_{1/2}$; thus the total number of atoms is $A \cdot T_{1/2}/0.693$.

Thus 1 mCi of radium contains $N = 3.7 \times 10^7 \times 1,600 \times 365 \times 24 \times 3,600/0.693$ atoms which is equivalent to a mass of $N \times 226/A_0$ gram (where A is Avogadro's number) = 1 milligram.

But 1 mCi of Phosphorus-32 (half-life 14 days) only contains a fraction $(14/1,600 \times 365) \times (32/226)$ of the mass of the same activity of radium, i.e. 3×10^6 mg.

The quantity $\bar{T} = T_{1/2}/0.693$ is given the name mean life since it is as if all the atoms had a life time $\bar{T}$ at which point they all suddenly decay (see fig. 2-5a).

CHAPTER 3

Radiotherapy

THE DISCOVERY OF X-RAYS AND RADIOACTIVITY

Before explaining how an object emits radiations, let us look into the history of the discovery of these types of radiation at the end of the last century. Various phenomena involving electrical forces had been studied during the late-eighteenth and early-nineteenth centuries and the workers who contributed to the knowledge of electricity and the ways in which it could be controlled have names that are now familiar in the units of electricity: Volta, Ohm, Faraday and Ampère. There developed at this time a certain fascination in the phenomena that arise when an electric current passes from one electrode to another in a partially evacuated tube. The residual gases in the tube exhibited characteristic effects including the emission of light and luminous striation patterns as the tube was further evacuated. With very little gas in the tube the glass surrounding the positive electrode was seen to fluoresce; this was due to the electrons passing right across the tube and striking the glass. The fact that it was electrons causing these effects was not realised until later; the workers in this field called the radiation passing across the tube cathode rays, because they were seen to originate from the cathode.

The strange thing was that none of the people who observed these effects and demonstrated the properties of cathode rays realised that another, far more important radiation, was being emitted from the anode, due to the interaction of the cathode rays with the metal electrode. Although some of the investigators, including Crookes and Lenard, reported finding strangely fogged photographic plates in their laboratories, it was not until 1895 that Roentgen investigated these further emissions and identified the radiation as X, the unknown radiation. He discovered that this had the properties of penetrating wood, cloth and even human tissue to show the bones of the hand on a crude fluorescent screen. Immediately after Roentgen announced his discovery these rays were put into use by many workers, since the apparatus was already widely available but nobody had realised that these rays were emanating from it each time it was switched on. Diagnosis using X-rays developed rapidly from this time and the first treatments of cancer were done at the end of the nineteenth century and the beginning of the twentieth century.

Radioactive Materials

A few weeks after Roentgen's discovery Poincaré, a French physicist, suggested that naturally fluorescent substances should be investigated to see if they emitted similar radiations. Becquerel found, in 1896, that uranium salts spontaneously emitted radiations which blackened photographic film. At this time also Marie and Pierre Curie, names associated more widely with radioactivity, enter the story. Marie Curie tested many materials to see if they emitted radiations and found that thorium compounds were radioactive. She then found when examining pitchblende that there was more radiation emitted than could be accounted for by the known amount of uranium and thorium this ore contained. This inspired her search to isolate the substance that she knew must be a new element. The first element that she and her husband isolated, which they called polonium, was announced in 1898. Another new element, radium, for which discovery they are more widely known, was announced later the same year. The isolation of radium in quantity large enough to study its chemical properties occupied Marie Curie for most of her life.

The chemists having discovered these radioactive materials, the physicists now began to study the properties of the radiations emitted; the only properties so far recognised being the ability to blacken photographic plates and to cause a charged gold leaf electroscope to lose its charge. Rutherford, Geissler and Villard demonstrated that radioactive substances can emit three types of radiation differing greatly in their properties; they were named alpha, beta and gamma. Beta radiation was shown to be identical to an electron beam and to the cathode rays in the Crooke's tube; gamma rays were shown to have the same properties as X-rays. At a later date alpha particles were shown to be identical with the nuclei of helium. It is interesting to note that the properties of all these radiations were well known before any reliable hypothesis was made as to the origin of the radiation.

Atoms, Isotopes and Radioactivity

The hypothesis that matter is made up from discrete parts known as atoms is so old and commonplace that it is easy to forget the vast amount of thought and work that has been necessary to prove that atoms exist. The combination of nuclear physics and quantum mathematical theory showed the atom itself to be constructed from the basic particles: the neutron, the proton and the electron. We call these objects particles for convenience; since we cannot see what happens in the atom directly, a model must be designed, based on observed nuclear reactions, to which various ideas can be added as experimental evidence increases. The mass of an atom is mainly concentrated in the nucleus which contains neutrons and protons in approximately equal numbers. These particles can exist by themselves, but under the right conditions of nuclear forces they are combined to form stable nuclei. If a nucleus is surrounded by orbiting electrons an atom is formed. The concept of the electron orbiting the nucleus, in the same way as a satellite orbits the earth, is to simplify the description to make an easier model to understand. It is more important at higher levels of discussion in nuclear physics to talk in terms of energy levels of electrons within the atom.

Some Particular Atoms

The simplest of all atoms is that of hydrogen containing one proton and one electron. The next element on the scale is helium with two protons and two neutrons (see fig. 3-1). The atomic mass of an element is the total number of protons and neutrons (atomic mass of helium equals four); the atomic number is the number of electrons orbiting the nucleus (for helium this is two). In chemical reactions it is the atomic number that is important since it is the electrons that interact with each other; in the study of radioactivity it is usually the atomic mass that is important as this determines the type of radioactive disintegration that will occur. A common element is that of carbon (see fig. 3-1(c)); it will be noticed that the inner orbit contains only two electrons. This is the maximum number of electrons allowed to exist in the inner orbit. These electrons enjoy the closest interaction with the nucleus and so have the highest energy (binding energy). The orbit of any electron is not fixed in one plane; the plane rotates continuously about the axis of the nucleus forming a complete shell around the nucleus.

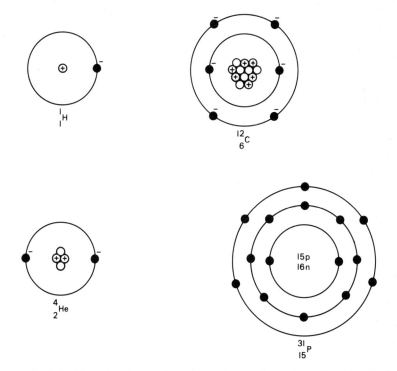

Fig. 3.1. The structure of certain atoms. $\oplus$ *proton,* $\circ$ *neutron,* $\bullet$
electron.

The inner electron orbits are known as the K shell, the next
orbits are called the L shell and can contain eight electrons, the
next is the M shell and so on; all these shells can contain eight
electrons.

Natural and Artificial Radioactivity

As a result of research on naturally occurring radioactive
elements, it was shown that each radioactive nuclide is a
member of one of three long decay chains: beginning with
uranium, actinium or thorium, which all have very long half-
lives ($T_{1/2} = 10^9$ years), which is the reason for the existence of
all the decay products at the present time. The end point of all
these series after various decays is one of the stable isotopes of
lead. Any naturally occurring isotopes other than these
generally have an atomic number of less than two hundred and
are caused by cosmic irradiation in the outer layers of the

atmosphere, e.g. carbon-14 is produced from stable carbon-12 in carbon dioxide.

All other isotopes which are radioactive are formed artificially. They generally are of low or medium atomic number and emit beta rays, positrons or gamma rays, rather than alpha particles. It is possible to produce almost any radioisotope by either bombarding a substance with neutrons or charged particles, or obtaining it as a fission product from a nuclear reactor. In general bombardment with neutrons produces nuclides with a neutron excess; charged particle collisions produce neutron deficient nuclides. The constitution of both natural and artificial nuclides can be shown on a graph in which the number of neutrons is plotted against the number of protons (fig. 3-2). The stable nuclides follow a definite line. The unstable nuclides lie to either side of this line; those with an excess number of neutrons above the line, those deficient in neutrons below the line. Any radioactive decay process tends to produce a change in the nuclide so that the product nuclide is nearer the position of the line of stable nuclides. Thus nuclides with a neutron excess are beta emitters and the product nuclide has one more proton (the movement is down and to the right), a nuclide deficient in neutrons is a positron emitter and the product nuclide has one less proton (the movement is up and to the left).

Radioactivity

Beta emission

A stable nucleus is one in which the nuclear forces binding the nucleons (the neutrons and protons) together are balanced by the electromagnetic forces exerted by the charged protons. As long as no violent force intervenes to disturb this stability these enormous forces containing the nucleons do not allow any change to take place. If the balance of energy in the nucleus is disturbed by the introduction of, say, an extra neutron, then the nucleus becomes unstable or radioactive and will spontaneously change at any moment in time, to return to its stable state. For example: consider the isotope of phosphorous $^{31}_{15}P$, containing 15 protons and 17 neutrons (atomic number 15, atomic mass 31); if one neutron is added to this it becomes radioactive $^{32}_{15}P$ that decays into $^{32}_{16}S$ (stable sulphur). The extra neutron has changed into a proton by emitting a beta particle. In fact protons and neutrons are obviously very similar particles because they can change into each other and emit

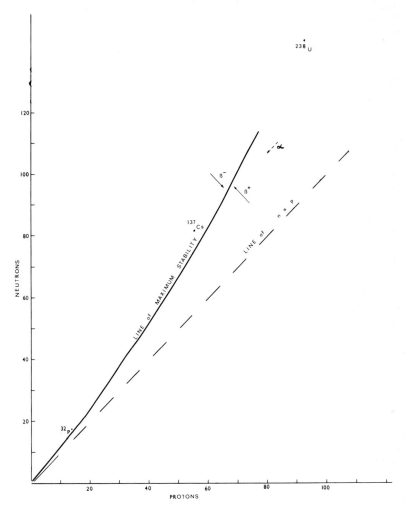

Fig. 3.2. A graph of number of neutrons against number of protons.

radiations of a similar nature: this can be shown by the equations:

$$n \rightarrow p + e^- \text{ (emitting beta particles or electrons)}$$

$$p \rightarrow n + e^+ \text{ (emitting positions).}$$

Notice that in these equations the total charge is the same on each side.

Gamma-emission

Another type of radioactivity is that where gamma rays are emitted. This type of emission takes place when a nucleus has too much energy and has to rid itself of this excess by emitting a gamma photon (a bundle of energy). This process usually occurs in radioactive substances that emit beta rays or protons as well; immediately following the emission of a beta particle the nucleus is in an excited state, it returns to an unexcited state by emitting a gamma photon, e.g.

$$^{60}_{27}Co \rightarrow {}^{60}_{28}Ni^* + e^-$$

$$^{60}_{28}Ni^* \rightarrow {}^{60}_{28}Ni + \gamma$$

(* Excited State).

notice that once the beta ray has been emitted there is no further change in atomic number or atomic mass when the gamma ray is emitted. This gamma ray has a definite amount of energy which is the same for every atom of a given isotope. Gamma radiation is thus said to have line energy spectra, i.e. if the number of photons per disintegration of a particular energy is plotted against energy a number of lines result depending on the isotope (see fig. 3-3).

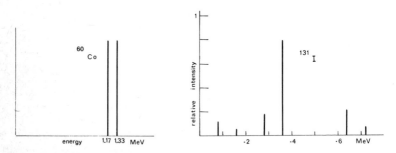

Fig. 3.3.   *The line spectra of cobalt-60 and iodine 131.*

Neutrons

Radiation beams of neutrons are already beginning to be used in radiotherapy. It is possible that they may be more successful in treating certain types of tumours, those containing anoxic regions, than X- or gamma rays. Neutrons are spontaneously emitted from radioactive isotopes of high atomic number and it is these materials that are used in nuclear reactors. However, these are low-energy neutrons with energies of the order of a few eV and are not suitable for treatment. High energy neutrons (30 MeV) for treatment are produced in a cyclotron in which protons are accelerated to a sufficiently high energy to react with targets to give off neutrons. Accelerating tubes have also been produced for generating neutrons. The tube is similar to a medium energy X-ray tube but contains deuterium. A high-frequency electrical field applied across the tube causes deuterons to form which are accelerated by a high potential of about 150 kV to strike a target containing tritium. The nuclear reaction that takes place (d, n) releases neutrons with energy of about 14 MeV, which have a penetration into body tissue similar to 4 MeV X-rays. A longer lasting tube now available contains a mixed beam of deuterium and tritium ions and a target containing tritium. A typical output of this tube is about 5 rads/min at a treatment distance of 100 cm. This appears very low, but the biological effect of neutrons means that the effective dose rate is 10-20 times greater.

There is also now a neutron emitting nuclide suitable for interstitial therapy, the transuranium element californium-252. This decays by alpha emission and spontaneous fission with a half-life of 2.58 years. The neutron flux is 2.34×10^{12} neutrons/sec for 1 gram of californium. The mean neutron energy is 2.3 MeV. This nuclide has been made into needles similar to radium needles; a 10 μg needle produces a dose rate of 20 rad/hour at one centimetre.

Alpha particles

The only other type of radiation which should be mentioned here is alpha radiation. An isotope which emits alpha particles is radium which decays to radon according to the following equation:

$$^{226}_{88}\text{Ra} \rightarrow \,^{222}_{86}\text{Rn} + \,^{4}_{2}\text{He}(\alpha\text{-particle}).$$

Notice that both the atomic numbers and atomic masses balance on both sides of this equation. The alpha particle is in fact a helium nucleus.

The Properties of Radiations and Their Interaction with Matter
The most basic properties of the radiations described above can be shown by the following table:

Radiation	Charge	Mass
Gamma	0	0
Beta	−1	1/1840
Alpha	+2	4
Neutron	0	1
Proton	+1	1

The Charged Particles
These have the facility, owing to forces of attraction or repulsion, of removing electrons from atoms to form ions. The faster a charged particle is travelling (i.e. the more energy it has), the further it can travel into the absorbing material, giving up some of its energy at each production of an ion. As it slows it produces more and more ions for equal distances travelled; this idea can be illustrated by the Bragg curve of ionisation for a charged particle (see fig. 3-4). Electrons produce ionisation of relatively low linear density as shown in the figure. Alpha

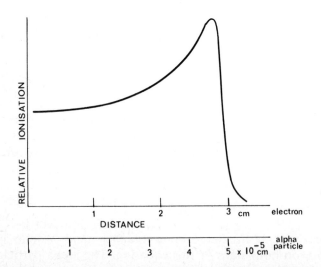

Fig. 3.4. A Bragg ionisation curve showing the difference in scale between the range of an electron (6 MeV) and that of an alpha particle (6 MeV).

particles, because of their large mass compared with an electron and their double charge, travel more slowly for a given energy (kinetic energy = $\frac{1}{2}mv^2$) than electrons and produce much denser ionisation. With any charged particle interactions with matter it is the ionisation that plays the vital part in producing radiation effects.

The Uncharged Particles

Both photons (X-ray photons or gamma-ray photons) and neutrons are indirectly ionising radiations; they do not produce large numbers of ions themselves, but they interact with matter (see Chapter 2) to produce charged particles that in turn ionise the material. Photons have to actually collide with the electrons surrounding atoms to give up their energy. This is a random interaction governed by the laws of probability and loss of photons from a beam interacting with matter follows an exponential law. Thus some photons may interact immediately they enter a medium, others may pass right through without any interaction. Generally it can be seen that photons can penetrate deep into tissue. Neutrons follow similar laws of interaction, but interact mainly with the protons in the nuclei of atoms. The protons, being charged particles, have an ionisation curve similar to alpha particles but are much more penetrating as they have a quarter the mass and half the charge of an alpha particle.

Summary:

$$\left.\begin{array}{l} \text{X-rays} \\ \text{gamma-photons} \end{array}\right\} \xrightarrow{\text{matter}} \text{electrons} \xrightarrow{\text{matter}} \text{ions}$$

$$\text{neutrons} \xrightarrow{\text{matter}} \text{protons} \xrightarrow{\text{matter}} \text{ions}$$
$$\text{alpha particles} \xrightarrow{\text{matter}} \text{ions}$$

EFFECTS OF IONISATION

Photographic Action

X-rays have a similar effect on photographic film to that of light. Film exposed to X-rays is blackened to an extent depending on the length of exposure, radiation intensity and type (*quality*) of radiation. This subject is discussed in detail in Chapter 5.

Chemical Action

One of the important chemical reactions produced by radiation is the oxidation of ferrous sulphate to ferric sulphate:

$$Fe^{++} \xrightarrow{\text{radiation}} Fe^{+++}.$$

This reaction is the basis of an absolute measure of radiation dose (see below). Another result of the irradiation of a medium is the production of highly active free radicals: atoms or molecules without some of their outer electrons, that are powerfully reactive.

Biological Action

The interaction of radiation with human tissue is the essential property that determines the usefulness of radiation for radio-therapy. There appear to be two main effects of this inter-action: (i) indirect action, where the damaging of a living cell subsequent to radiation is brought about by chemical changes due to the production of free radicals; (ii) direct action, where the direct hit on a vulnerable point within a complex molecule prevents the living cell from performing its function correctly, thus stopping it reproducing and so in effect killing it. The details of these effects cannot be discussed here but two points

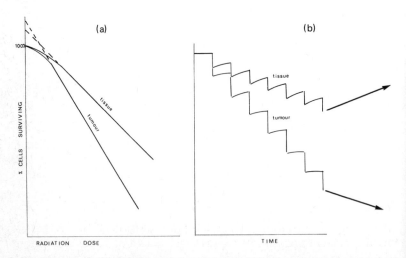

Fig. 3.5. (a) The difference in radiosensitivity between tumour and normal tissue. (b) The effect of a number of equal doses given over a period of time (fractionation).

important to radiotherapy must be made clear: (i) that all cells are not killed simultaneously, (ii) that some cells are more easily killed than others (they are more radiosensitive). The latter fact allows the required collection of cells (the tumour) to be destroyed while only partially damaging normal tissue (see fig. 3-5a, b). Of course, if it were possible to irradiate tumour only, normal tissue need not be damaged; but in most cases this is impossible. In radiotherapy the amount of radiation is measured in terms of absorbed dose, this is the energy absorbed by the tissue from the radiation beams. The tumour volume is irradiated to a known optimum level of dose by treatment to a well-tried regime. (See section on fractionation.)

RADIATIONS USED IN RADIOTHERAPY

Internal Radiation
Nearly all radiotherapy of tumours inside the body is achieved using radioactive materials. The most commonly used until recently was radium in the form of needles and tubes that could be placed in the body in various arrangements to give a very high local dose to the tumour (5,000 to 10,000 rads), but with a very rapid fall-off (due to inverse square law) with distance from the tumour, so that tissues even as close as 10 cm to the tumour only receive a few hundred rads. Other radioactive materials now used and the types of treatment given may be summarised in a table:

Radio nuclide	Radiation	Form used
Caesium-137	Gamma	Needles and tubes
Cobalt-60	Gamma	Beads and tubes
Gold-198	Gamma	Seeds for permanent implantation
Tantalum-182	Gamma	Wire
Strontium-90	Beta	Eye applicator
Phosphorus-32	Beta	Injection—attaches itself to red blood cells to treat polycythaemia
Iodine-131	Beta	Orally to treat thyroid disorders

More details of the use of these nuclides are given in Chapter 4.

External Beam
To treat deep-seated tumours, it can be seen that very penetrating beams are necessary, otherwise only a very small

proportion of the radiation will reach the tumour. X- and gamma-photon beams are the most commonly used, although neutrons are beginning to be used. X-rays are generated at different energies depending on the treatment site.

For very superficial skin treatments   10-30 kV
Superficial energy therapy   60-140 kV
Medium energy therapy   200-300 kV
Megavoltage therapy   2-8 MV

The gamma rays from the nuclides cobalt-60 and caesium-137 are also used for external beam radiotherapy.

KILOVOLTAGE X-RAY THERAPY EQUIPMENT

X-ray Tubes
Generally the X-ray tubes used for treatment are similar to the stationary anode tubes that are used in diagnostic sets, i.e. they basically consist of a filament that emits electrons which are accelerated across an evacuated tube to strike the anode to produce X-rays (fig. 3-6). The filament is a small coil of

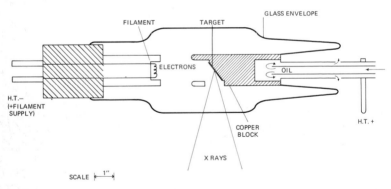

Fig. 3.6. An X-ray therapy tube for production of 250 kV X-rays.

tungsten wire which can provide high electron emission. This is usually set into a metal housing which is at a different potential from the filament, providing an initial focusing effect on the stream of electrons. The target is also made of tungsten because a high atomic number material provides efficient X-ray production; it also has a high melting point (3,380°C) allowing it to be heated to high temperatures by the bombardment of elec-

trons without distortion of its shape. Cooling of the target and
anode assembly is provided by oil which either flows through
the tube housing, as is usual in 250 kV machines, or remains
stationary and is in turn cooled by water, as in the 60-140 kV
machine. Oil must be used since it is an insulator and in most of

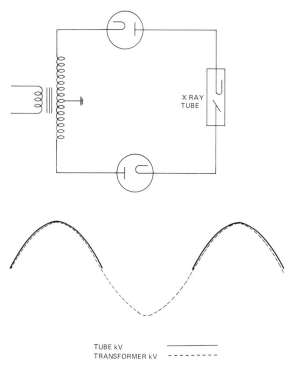

TUBE kV ————————
TRANSFORMER kV - - - - - - - -

Fig. 3.7. A 2-rectifier generating circuit for production of low energy
X-rays.

these X-ray machines both the anode and the cathode are at a
high potential with respect to earth; this is because the generator circuit is as shown in fig. 3-7, so that only half the full
potential is applied to each cable. There are some target-earthed
machines where the filament is at the full potential, so the cable
to the cathode has to withstand this potential; the targets of
these machines can then be water cooled as the anode is at earth
potential.

The X-ray tube and the tube housing are designed to prevent any possibility of the high-voltage sparking between anode and cathode. The tube itself is often of a re-entrant type to provide a long path length between the electrodes externally without increasing the distance between the filament and the anode. The higher the voltage to be used the longer the tube must be. The tube is completely surrounded by the insulating oil which must not be allowed to overheat or become dirty as its insulating property will be impaired and sparking between electrodes may occur. The tube connectors are held well away from the tube housing to prevent any likelihood of sparking between an electrode and the metal housing which must be at earth potential. As well as providing an electrical shield for the tube and a certain amount of mechanical protection, the tube housing contains a lead lining to protect the patient from unwanted stray radiation.

A Machine for Superficial Treatment

For treatment of skin and other treatments where the lesion to be treated is superficial, little penetration of the X-rays is desirable and most sets are designed to work in the range 60-140 kV and at short distances of 15-20 cm Focus–Skin–Distance (FSD). With these conditions the 50% dose level occurs at between 1 and 4 cm depth depending on field size and X-ray energy (see fig. 3-8). The HT generator is usually a simple two-valve circuit, as shown in the figure, with facilities for controlling the kilovoltage and the tube current from outside the treatment room. The tube housing is mounted on an arm either from a wall mounting or a pedestal; this provides movements that allow the X-ray beam to be pointed in almost any direction. The oil in the tube housing is cooled by water passing through a copper coil immersed in the oil.

Filtration

As the kilovoltage increases it is desirable to remove the lower X-ray energies by filtration so that the required dose at a depth is achieved without unnecessary increase in the dose to the skin. In the range 60-120 kV filtration is satisfactorily achieved with aluminium 0.5-2.0 mm thick; at 140 kV a filter of 0.25 mm copper plus 1.0 mm aluminium is more suitable, producing the effect on the X-ray spectrum shown in fig. 3-9. These filters are

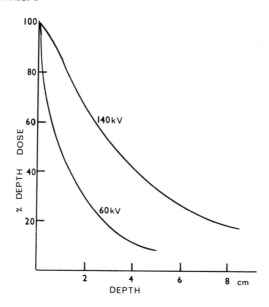

*Fig. 3.8. Typical % depth dose curves for 60 kV (3 cm diam field) and
140 kV (8 cm diam. field) at 15 cm. Focus–Skin–Distance (F.S.D.).*

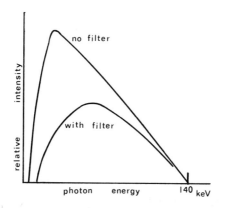

*Fig. 3.9. The effect of filtration on a continuous X-ray spectrum. The
peak of this curve moves towards the right so increasing the effective energy.*

mounted in the tube head in front of the X-ray window. An interlock system should be provided so that the machine cannot be switched on unless the correct filter is in place.

Applicators
A range of applicators of various diameters is used to provide a choice of field size to fit over the lesion. It is desirable for these to have perspex ends as this facilitates the positioning of the applicator. If the correct size of applicator is not available or if the treatment area is not circular lead masks are made from lead 0.5-1 mm thick. The dose rate at the end of each applicator is measured for each X-ray energy and a chart constructed for use by the radiographers. It is usual to have a timer attached to the control circuit to switch the X-rays off after the time needed to give the prescribed dose.

A MEDIUM ENERGY MACHINE
For treatment of tumours at depths up to 5 cm, X-rays need to be generated at potentials 200 to 300 kV. The X-ray tubes in these machines usually work at a tube current of about 15 mA. As most of the electrons give up their energy in the target as heat, energy is dissipated in the target at the rate of working similar to that of an electric fire. This heat must be removed by conduction along the copper stem which in turn is cooled by a continuous flow of oil. The oil is cooled in a heat exchanger by a cold-water flow usually directly from the mains.

To achieve the high potential necessary in these machines various electrical circuits have been designed. One of these is the Greinacher circuit (see fig. 3-10) in which the condensers hold the charge from one half of the alternating cycle so that on the next half-cycle the voltage across both condensers is double the voltage on the secondary winding of the transformer. If the transformer is centre-tapped only half of the final voltage needed is applied to each electrode of the X-ray tube. Thus if 300 kV is required only 75 kV need be generated at the transformer. With this lower voltage there is much less likelihood of breakdown of the various parts in the generator. In these machines it may be several seconds before the full kilovoltage is achieved; for this reason a shutter is employed that is only opened when the full potential is developed across the tube. The shutter operation is usually synchronous with the switching on of the timer.

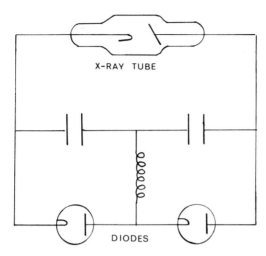

Fig. 3.10. A Greinacher generating circuit.

These machines are usually gantry mounted with a motor driven vertical movement, movements along two axes and rotation about two axes, so that the X-ray head can be positioned to point along any path required. The X-ray beam is defined by a choice of circular or rectangular applicators, to be used in contact with the skin at a treatment distance of 50 cm from the source, giving depth dose curves as shown in fig. 3-11. These machines were originally developed for a range of energies from 140 kV to 250 kV and therefore they usually have a choice of filters which are carefully interlocked to prevent the wrong filter being used. The output varies considerably with filtration; at 250 kV 15 mA with no filter the output is about 300 rads/minute (this condition would not be used as too much soft radiation is emitted); when the beam is very heavily filtered, e.g. using 1.2 mm tin plus 0.25 mm copper plus 1 mm aluminium, the low energies are absorbed (see fig. 3-12) and the output falls to 30 rads/minute. However, this beam of radiation is penetrating and is not absorbed much more by bone than by soft tissue. The main disadvantages of this type of radiation are the low output, the lack of skin sparing, and the relatively large amount of side scatter (see isodose curve fig. 3-13) compared to high energy radiation.

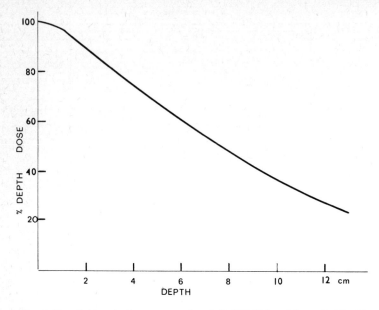

Fig. 3.11. % Depth dose curve for 250 kV (10 x 10 cm field) 50 cm F.S.D.

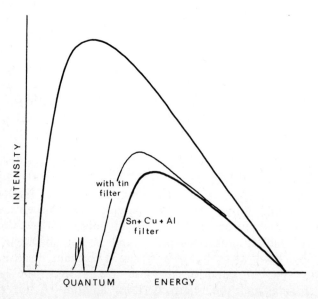

Fig. 3.12. The effect of a composite filter on 250 kV X-ray spectrum.

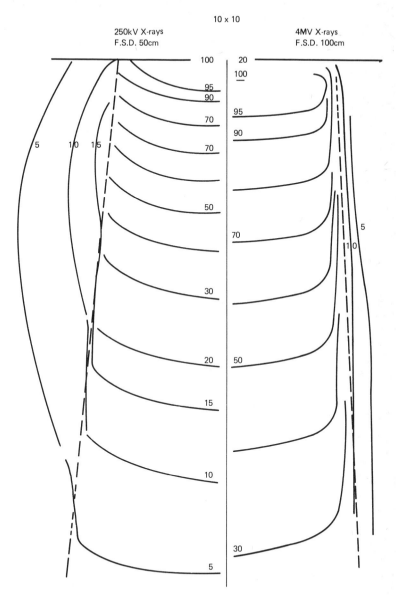

Fig. 3.13. A comparison of the isodose curves for 250 kV X-rays (H.V.L. = 3.5 mm Cu) against 4 MV X-rays (H.V.L. = 16 mm Cu).

HIGH ENERGY RADIATION THERAPY

High-energy beams of X-rays (from linear accelerators or beta-trons) and gamma rays (e.g. cobalt-60) are now available and have a number of advantages particularly for beam directional radiotherapy. These are:

(1) greater % depth dose,
(2) skin sparing—this is due to the build-up effect,* the peak dose appears at a point below the skin surface (e.g. 0.5 cm for cobalt-60, 2 cm for 8 MV X-rays) which means that large doses can be given without producing severe skin erythema,
(3) high output even at long treatment distance,
(4) the normal treatment distance (100 cm) allows the machine to be rotated around the patient, which eases patient positioning,
(5) less side-scatter than medium-energy beams.

Isotope Machines for External Therapy

The strange thing about radiation energies used in radiotherapy is that there is a range from 300 kV to 1 MV that is hardly used. This is a result of the development of machines for radio-therapy. For the X-ray tube and generator to be used at voltages above 300 kV the problems of insulation become great. The linear electron accelerator was developed before it was neces-sary to consider these problems. However, there is a radioactive isotope with a gamma-ray energy in this region; caesium-137 has a gamma-ray energy of 660 keV. This would be very useful in radiotherapy as it would have sufficient penetration for deep-seated tumours, there is some skin sparing and it has a long half-life of 30 years. Unfortunately, as a sufficiently high specific activity of caesium-137 in the source cannot be attained to give a satisfactory dose rate at the usual megavoltage treatment distance of a 100 cm, it is only used rarely for external therapy. Treatment distances of 30 to 40 cm are used, but even at these distances the output is only 30-50 rads/minute with a source activity of 1,500 curies.

The isotope that is used widely for external beam radio-therapy is cobalt-60. This emits 2 gamma rays of 1.17 and 1.33 MeV (fig. 3-2). Cobalt-60 is produced in a nuclear reactor by

---

* The build-up effect is due to the relatively long path length and predominantly forward direction of the secondary electrons.

bombarding the common isotope of cobalt with neutrons. The neutron flux has to be sufficiently high to build up a usable activity of cobalt-60 within the period of its half-life which is five years. For treatment purposes the isotope is contained in the head of the machine within a lead-filled steel protective case. There are various arrangements in different machines for bringing this source rapidly into a position opposite an opening

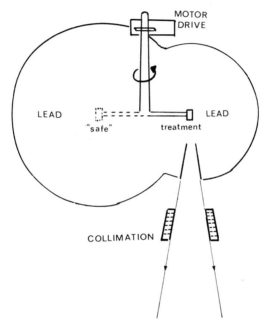

Fig. 3.14. A cobalt-60 treatment head showing the source in the treatment position.

in the head, so that a controllable beam of radiation emerges. One of the simplest ways, shown in fig. 3-14, is to mount the source on a wheel which is electrically driven through 180° to carry the source from its safe position to the treatment position. This source wheel usually contains a fail-safe device, such as some form of spring loading, in case the power to the motor drive fails. The simple operation of these machines means that they need very little maintenance compared to linear accelerators.

The other design features of cobalt-60 machines are very

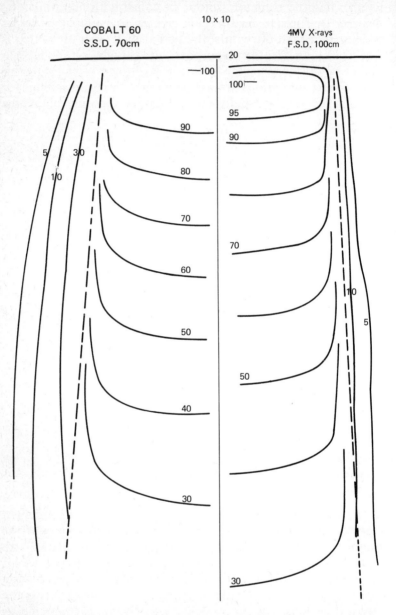

Fig. 3.15. A comparison of isodose curves—cobalt-60 against 4 MV X-rays.

similar to linear accelerators. The treatment distance is 70-100 cm with an output of 80-140 rads/min, for source activities in the range 4,000-5,000 curies.

The isodose curves are very similar to those for 4 MV X-rays (see fig. 3-15), in that the penetration is the same, however there is a larger penumbra due to the source having a diameter of about 2 cm. This penumbra can be reduced by extra collimation close to the patient (see fig. 3-16), but these penumbra trimmers have to be removable so that it is possible to rotate the machine round the patient.

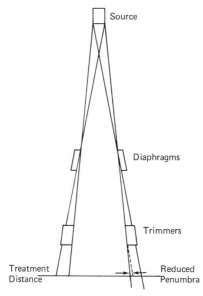

Fig. 3.16. The effect of trimmers on the penumbra of a cobalt-60 source.

The Electron Linear Accelerator

The method of production of radiation from the electron linear accelerator is the same as that of the X-ray tube in that electrons are accelerated *in vacuo* from an electron filament to strike a target to produce X-rays. The principle is different, however, as the electrons are transported by a travelling electro-magnetic field of radiation (radio waves of very high power) instead of being accelerated by a static high voltage electric field.

The central part of the accelerator is the wave guide (see fig. 3-17). This is an evacuated cylindrical tube that acts as a conducting guide of the radio waves. At one end is the electron gun containing a filament from which electrons are ejected; at the other end is an X-ray transmission target—a thin disc of tungsten-copper alloy—since at the electron energies these accelerators produce, the X-rays are given off from the target mainly in the forward direction. The electrons enter the guide at an energy of about 40 keV and are transported by the radio waves, which accelerate the electrons to reach nearly the speed of light at the target. The electrons reach the end of the guide with energies in the range 4-20 MeV depending on the length of the guide; the X-rays given off thus have a spectrum of energies with the maximum energy being the maximum electron energy.

There are many parts to a linear accelerator and some of the most recently designed have very complex control circuits; but some essential factors appear in all machines. The radio frequency waves are usually produced by a magnetron valve that produces powerful enough waves to transport the electrons by emitting energy in short bursts or pulses. These travel within a rectangular wave guide to the accelerating tube. The radio waves lose most of their energy transporting the electrons along the guide, the remaining energy is channelled away to a water or air absorbing load, in which the energy can be dissipated. The electrons are emitted from the filament of the electron gun in a narrow beam initially travelling in the static electric field produced by the 40 kV potential of the gun, then being picked up by the electromagnetic field (the waves) of the travelling wave. Within the evacuated tube this beam of electrons would have a tendency to diverge and become generally less compact due to the remaining molecules of air scattering the electrons in all directions; this is prevented by a series of focusing electromagnetic coils set around the guide. This compact beam will not necessarily travel straight along the guide, so it is necessary to provide centring magnetic fields at right angles to each other that can be adjusted to guide the beam most efficiently from one end of the guide to the other.

Beyond the target of the accelerator there is a conical primary-collimator to guide the primary beam of X-rays emitted from the target; this is made of heavily absorbing material such as lead and is of sufficient thickness to prevent appreciable radiation escaping in the wrong directions. If this were not

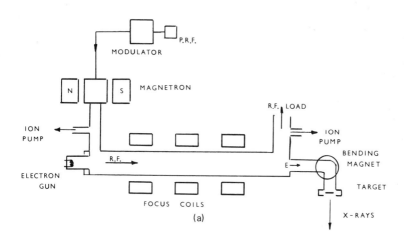

(a)

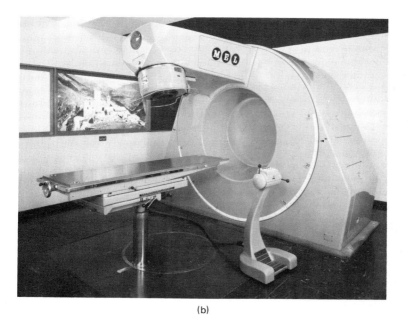

(b)

Fig. 3.17. (a) The essential parts of a linear accelerator. Radio frequency waves (R.F.) transport electrons (E) along waveguide. (b) Photograph of Linear Accelerator (Courtesy M. E. L. Philips).

provided the 'patient would receive a high dose of radiation to
his whole body that could produce radiation sickness before the
treated volume had received sufficient dose; also the walls of
the treatment room would have to be more absorbing to
prevent radiation escaping.

The intensity profile of the beam at the end of the primary
collimator is shown in fig. 3-18. This does not allow uniform
dosage to be attained over the treatment volume; so the beam is

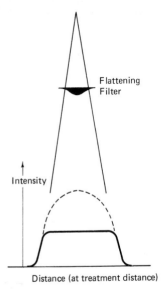

Fig. 3.18. *The effect of a flattening filter on the intensity of a high
energy X-ray beam. Without filter (dotted); with (solid).*

usually flattened by means of a conical-shaped piece of brass to
produce a flat beam profile.

The therapist must know accurately how much dose he is
giving to the patient. This could be estimated with a timer, as
on the cobalt machines, but the dose rate on an accelerator is
usually high (200-300 rads/min) and can vary during the period
of irradiation. A monitor ionisation chamber placed in the beam
to measure the radiation dose is the most satisfactory method.
This can be preset to stop the X-rays after a prescribed dose has
been given to the patient. Recently a radiation protection
committee has specified the requirements for dose monitoring

on this type of equipment, stipulating that there should be two independent ionisation chambers, in case one fails during an exposure, and also a timer in case both chambers fail.

The size of the radiation field needs to be continuously variable over the range of areas 3 x 3 cm to 30 x 30 cm at the patient's skin. This is achieved with two pairs of diaphragms, driven by special gearing either by hand or motor, to give square or rectangular fields. The size of the field is shown by dials on the X-ray head. There is usually also a light beam that shows the path of the X-ray beam by a carefully positioned lamp and mirror; this gives the radiographer a rectangle of light to position on the patient's skin; it also shows the central axis of

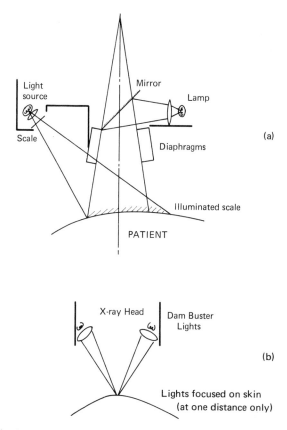

Fig. 3.19. (a) A linear accelerator treatment head showing the light beam diaphragm system and the illuminated scale which acts as a front pointer. (b) Dam buster lights for focusing at one distance only.

the beam as the shadow of a cross on a graticule. Another device essential for the accurate positioning of patients is an optical front pointer: this can take the form of "dam buster" lights, or a projected light scale (see fig. 3-19). This allows the patient's skin to be positioned at a known distance from the X-ray source, at a point where the dose rate is accurately known.

The movements of the machine and treatment table are such as to allow the X-ray beam to pass into the patient along almost any path the therapist desires. This means that the X-ray head must be able to be set at any angle and it is usual for it to rotate about a point in space known as the isocentre of the machine (see fig. 3-20), since the treatment table also rotates about this point. This makes patient positioning much easier as it limits the degrees of freedom of movement. It also allows the isocentre to be positioned at the tumour centre to make multiple beam direction treatments simpler. Very accurate machining is necessary to allow a treatment head and associated equipment weighing up to two tons to rotate around a point to an accuracy of a few millimetres.

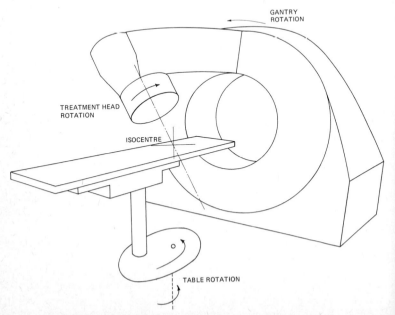

Fig. 3.20. The principle of isocentric mounting showing how the gantry, head and table all rotate about the same point.

In the most recent linear accelerators the accelerating wave guide is mounted horizontally and the electrons are bent through an angle of about 90 degrees by a magnetic field before striking the X-ray target. These machines can rotate all the way round the patient. With the vertical accelerating waveguide there is a limit on the angle to which the head can be moved. Even if part of the floor is removed the maximum angle is about 140 degrees from the vertical, since the patient must be easily accessible for positioning by radiographers.

Radiotherapy Procedure

There are two main types of treatment in radiotherapy: radical and palliative. The object of radical therapy is to deliver a certain minimum dose to the whole growth which is of a magnitude which ensures that all the malignant cells are killed or are so damaged that they are unable to survive. In general this dose will be near the limit of normal tissue tolerance, and it is important not to exceed this limit. Palliative therapy, as the term suggests, is not intended to cure the disease, but to improve the patient's comfort particularly by reducing the size of a tumour.

Fractionation

In radical therapy the level of dose to give has been determined over the years from experience with patients. A tumour can be treated with a single dose of radiation, but unless the growth is only a small skin tumour the dose needed to kill the tumour cannot be tolerated by the surrounding tissues. The majority of tumours are best treated by fractionating the treatment into a number of fractions over a period of time, e.g., twenty fractions are given daily for four weeks. This method of treatment gives the maximum benefit from the difference in radiosensitivity between normal and abnormal tissue. The normal tissues are less easily damaged than the cells of the tumour and tend to recover at a faster rate. There has been a lot of discussion concerning fractionation recently since Ellis[1] derived the formula:

$$D = NSD \cdot T^{0.11} \cdot N^{0.24};$$

where T = time in days, N = number of fractions, NSD = Nominal Standard Dose, and different fractionation schemes can be

[1] Ellis, F (1969) Clinical Radiology **20**, 1-7

attempted to attain the same *NSD* with at least an approximate idea that the final result will be similar to if not better than the present. The formula suggests that if the dose is constant the effect of increasing the time is small after thirty days and that it is the number of fractions given in this time which determines the effect of the dose.

TREATMENT PLANNING

Superficial Therapy

All tumours treated by superficial therapy are close to the skin surface and are treated by using a single radiation field. The area to be treated is marked out on the patient's skin by the radiotherapist. If this area is small and circular an applicator of the correct diameter is chosen and applied directly on to the skin to cover the tumour; if the area is several centimetres across and irregularly shaped it is usual to use a lead mask cut to the shape of the tumour and then to apply an applicator of diameter greater than the cut-out. As the maximum dose is at the skin surface, this is the point at which the dose is prescribed. Some parts of the tumour may receive as much as 20-30% less than this dose, but the tolerance of skin to radiation is the limiting factor in superficial therapy. The prescribed dose may be given in several different regimes (see section on fractionation), e.g.: every day for ten or more days, three times a week for several weeks, or in a single treatment.

Medium Energy Therapy

Before the advent of megavoltage equipment medium-energy (250 kV to 300 kV) machines were used for all deep-seated tumours. The only way to obtain as high or a higher dose at the tumour than at the skin was to use two or more beams of radiation pointing at the tumour (see fig. 3-21). This could be done fairly accurately using angles and various gadgets to align the beam such as the back-pointer and the pin and arc. For checking positioning of fields radiographs were taken with the beam pointing in the desired direction and an X-ray film at the position where the beam emerged from the patient. For multi-field treatment plans a contour of the patient was taken in the plane of the central axes of the beams using lead-rubber strip. This material bends easily round corners, but maintains its shape so that it can be transferred to paper (fig. 3-22); patient thicknesses were checked with calipers to improve the accuracy

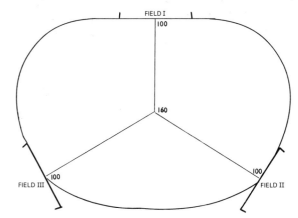

Fig. 3.21. A multiple beam treatment for 250 kV X-rays.

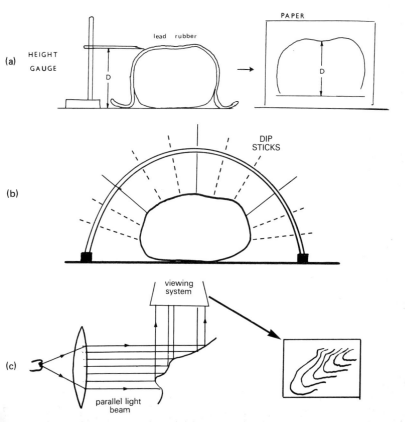

Fig. 3.22. Contouring devices. (a) Lead Rubber. (b) Dip sticks in frame. (c) Parallel Light—viewing contours at right angles.

of the contour. The beam size and direction were also transferred to the plan; the correct isodose curves could then be combined to form a complete pattern of depth doses (see below).

In centres where there is megavoltage apparatus there are not many multifield treatments on medium-energy apparatus since there are many advantages of using the higher-energy beams. Medium energy machines are then mostly used for single-field treatments where greater penetration is needed than is obtained on the superficial machines. The dose in this case is again prescribed at the skin as this receives the maximum dose. If a lead mask is necessary at this energy it needs to be 2 to 3 mm thick to reduce the stray radiation to 1 to 2% of the maximum dose.

Megavoltage Therapy

Treatment planning using high-energy beams must be very accurate so that the radiation is given precisely to the tumour volume and to the correct dose level prescribed by the therapist. It is possible to do this planning on the treatment machine itself, by directing the beam along the approximate path desired and taking radiographs, then changing the conditions if necessary and repeating this process until the optimum result is achieved. However, this is a very time-consuming and very wasteful use of an expensive machine. It is more usual to use a *simulator* on which to do the treatment planning, although there are certain circumstances when verification films taken on treatment machines are necessary, e.g. for mantle fields using lung shielding blocks. A simulator is a machine that reproduces as closely as possible all the movements of the treatment machine, but is much easier to position as the head only contains a diagnostic X-ray tube so that there is no need for heavy protection. All the planning of a patient can be done on this machine without holding up treatments on the treatment machines. The geometry of the X-ray beam must be the same as that on the treatment machine; however, this does not necessitate the use of movable diaphragms as the beam size can be shown simply by wire markers placed in the beam. The patient is positioned in the same way as on the treatment machine and radiographs are taken to check the beam size and direction. If planning is to be done reasonably quickly without the patient having to wait for the films to be developed, it is preferable to have some means of viewing the X-ray beam directly as it passes through the patient. This can be done using some form of fluoroscopy with an image intensifier. Further sophistication is achieved by being able to control all the movements of the simulator from the X-ray control, so that the beam can be driven into the correct position while observing the path it is following through the patient.

Once the therapist has confirmed that the positions and sizes of the X-ray beams are correct, it is possible to proceed with the next stage of the planning. The central axes of the beams and the beam edges are marked on the patient using the light beam of the simulator. A contour or contours of the patient in this treatment zone are then required. This can be done in one of a number of ways. Mechanical methods include the use of lead-rubber or dip-sticks (see fig. 3-22a, b). By illuminating the patient's surface with a sheet or sheets of light and viewing this image by a precise system, the contours may be displayed on a screen. If a set of parallel light beams at a known distance apart is used, the patient's surface photographed at right angles to the plane of light shows a series of contours (see fig. 3-22c), which is especially useful if a compensator is required for head and neck treatment (see below).

Combination of Isodose Curves

After the contour and any relevant skin marks have been transferred to paper the dosage calculation can begin. The direction of each beam is drawn and the correct isodose chart put in place along this direction. If multiple fields are used the depth doses are combined either by: (i) using an array of points and finding the contribution from each field to each point, then adding all these contributions together, or by: (ii) drawing out the isodose curves for each field and summing contributions at points of intersection of the curve. The latter method allows a total isodose curve to be drawn, by joining equal level points, without having to interpolate (see fig. 3-23).

In the majority of cases this is as much planning as is necessary, but in certain cases the complete plan is not satis- factory and it is necessary to change one or more of the conditions, e.g. a wedge angle or a beam direction. If the latter is necessary the patient must be returned to the simulator to verify the new beam direction. As for the plan, if the planners are very experienced they will be able to make the correct

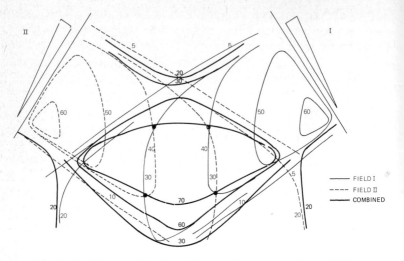

Fig. 3.23. The combination of two wedged megavoltage fields.

alterations to the plan fairly quickly. However, this is when a computer can be very useful in treatment planning. A computer system might be as follows, assuming the patient's contour is already drawn on paper: the contour is transferred to the computer memory using some electronic co-ordinate detector; the position, size and direction of the beams are also fed into the computer; the computer program will then take this information and using previously stored information of percentage depth dose, it will compute the total depth dose at a matrix of points. It is also possible to make the computer draw the patient's contour on to a screen and to program it to calculate and draw isodose levels on to this contour. This can all be done very rapidly; at the most it will take a few minutes compared to about half an hour by hand; and once the basic information has been stored in the computer for a particular patient a new set of isodose curves can be computed and drawn in a few seconds if only one parameter is changed.

When the plan has been drawn and the therapist is satisfied with the dose distribution, the dose to be given by each field is calculated and also the time or number of monitor units to be set on the therapy machine. The plan is then taken to the treatment machine and the radiographers can set the treatment machine according to the plan and so treat the patient precisely.

To improve on the precision of certain types of treatments various accessories are used, some of which are now described.

TREATMENT ACCESSORIES

The Head Shell
This is a device used to hold the head rigid so that beams of radiation may be directed along exactly the correct paths to

(a)

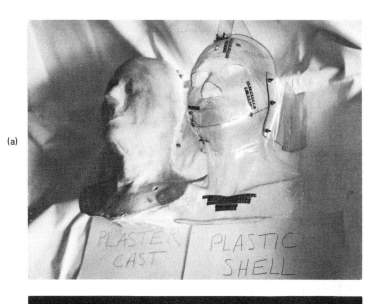

(b)

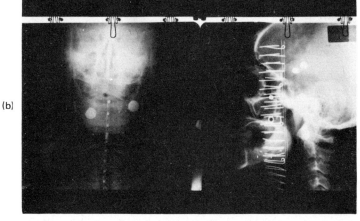

Fig. 3.24. (a) A plaster cast and head shell. (b) Radiographs for determining the position of the tumour with respect to surface markers.

cover the tumour. It is usually constructed from a lightweight, but easily moulded, plastic.[1] The various stages of constructing these shells are outlined below.

The therapist indicates the region of the head or neck he requires to be treated. A plaster-bandage shell is constructed over the relevant region by placing the bandages on the skin or, where the hair is involved, on a skull cap. This shell is used to mould a plaster cast of the patient's head and it is on this cast that the plastic shell is moulded, after the plastic has been heated to the correct temperature. When this shell has been suitably mounted in a position comfortable to the patient and convenient for the field arrangement required, two sets of markers are attached (see fig. 3-24) and X-rays are taken at right angles to each other to localise the tumour in three dimensions. Using the information from these films almost all the planning and positioning of the treatment beams can be done on the shell. When the positions have been decided the patient can be placed in the shell and the treatment beams verified by taking X-ray pictures on the simulator. If the therapist is satisfied that the tumour is being treated efficiently by these beams the position and size of each field and also its exit points are marked on the shell. A contour is then taken from the inside of the shell; the treatment plan can then be accurately computed.

Wax Blocks

Occasionally a therapist requires to treat with tangential fields so as to achieve a dose distribution which does not penetrate too deeply and is also high at the skin surface. Marks to indicate the entrance point of the beams cannot be placed on the skin, so a plastic shell of the patient in the region between the fields is made and a wax block built on to it which acts as bolus material and allows the beams to be positioned accurately (see fig. 3-25a).

The Breast Bridge

If wax is not required by the therapist on chest wall or breast treatments using tangential fields, a treatment jig, known as a bridge, is used (see fig. 3.25b). This has adjustable end plates on which the light beams of the machine can be positioned. It can be angled across the chest wall to take in the volume specified by the therapist.

[1] e.g. Cabulite®, May & Baker Ltd or Bexoid, BX Plastics Ltd.

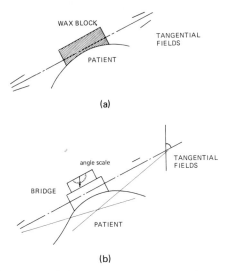

Fig. 3.25. (a) Tangential fields with a wax block. (b) Tangential fields with chest wall bridge.

Lead Blocks for Shielding

In a number of types of treatment, especially large field treatments, the therapist desires to shield certain parts of the body from radiation to prevent damage to organs in those parts. In Hodgkin's disease a large treatment field is used that includes the whole of the mediastinum, the supraclavicular and axillary regions and both sides of the neck, but shielding of the lungs is necessary. This can be done with lead blocks of about two-and-a-half inches thickness for 4 MV X-rays, which allow only 3% of the primary radiation to pass. To shield the lungs accurately these blocks need to be shaped for the individual patient. This can be done using the apparatus in fig. 3-26. The geometry of this is exactly the same as the treatment machine. The centre portion of the wire is electrical filament wire, so that when the current is on it can cut through the expanded polystyrene. A radiograph of the patient's chest, taken on the treatment machine, is placed at the correct distance and position with respect to the source. The lung areas, marked by the therapist, are then traced out and the wire simultaneously cuts the correct shape in the polystyrene. The resulting solid shapes can be embedded in sand and lead poured in, which melts the polystyrene and forms the correctly shaped lead blocks. Alter-

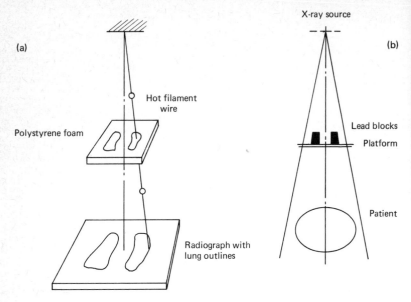

Fig. 3.26. (a) The cutting of polystyrene moulds for casting lead alloy
blocks. (b) The blocks in position on the platform of treatment machine.

natively the holes in the polystyrene can be used either by
filling them with lead shot (this requires a greater thickness for
the same attenuation as solid lead) or by using a special
low-melting-point lead alloy that will not melt the polystyrene.
A final check on the shape and position of the lead blocks can
be made by taking a radiograph with the patient on the
treatment machine itself.

Compensators

Instead of completely shielding parts of the beam, the therapist
sometimes requires modification of parts of the beam to
improve the dose distribution; this is especially true of head and
neck treatments where the patient's contour can be very
irregular. At medium energy X-rays there is no skin-sparing and
the contour can be levelled with wax (see fig. 3-27). However, if
skin-sparing is to be preserved on megavoltage treatments the
compensating material must be moved away from the skin to a
point at which most of the secondary electrons arising from the
compensator do not reach the skin. It is possible simply to
make a wax compensator on the surface of the patient and then

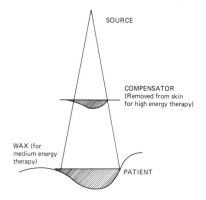

Fig. 3.27. A compensator for medium or high energy.

to move it about 20 cm from the skin; however, the geometry is altered due to the divergence of the beam. To build an accurate two-dimensional compensator a method of obtaining accurate contours in two dimensions is necessary. This information can then be used to build a compensator in aluminium, brass or lead, to be positioned at 20 to 40 cm from the skin surface.

MEASUREMENT OF RADIATION
Exposure Dose
The measurement of radiation quantity is made using the equivalent measurement of exposure with an ionisation chamber under equilibrium conditions.* For radiotherapy measurements this is usually an air-filled chamber of small dimensions; when radiation strikes the walls of the chamber electrons are produced that in turn ionise the gas within the air volume. The ionisation is measured using the circuit shown in fig. 3-28. If the central electrode is at a negative potential, positive ions are attracted to it to form a flow of charge along the conductor connected to the electrode. If an exposure dose is to be measured over a given time this charge is collected on a capacitor and the voltage across the capacitor is then directly proportional to the dose. The amount of charge is very small, of the order of 10^{-10} coulomb, so there must be no possibility of leakage current in the circuit. Thus the voltage must be measured with a high impedance electrometer. If it is desired to

---

* For equilibrium the number of electrons entering the measuring volume equals the number leaving.

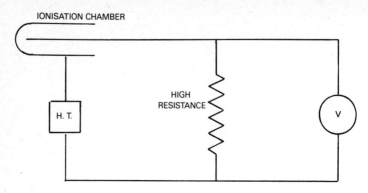

IONISATION CHAMBER

HIGH
RESISTANCE

H. T.

V

Fig. 3.28. The circuit for measuring ionisation current from an ionisation chamber.

measure dose rate the charge is allowed to flow through a high resistance to generate a voltage across it. This voltage is again measured by an electrometer. This type of small ionisation chamber and its associated electronics is used for all relative measurements of intensity within a radiation field; however, it can also be used for absolute measurement of dose.

Measurement of Absorbed Dose

As has been stated above the important parameter relating radiation to its effect is the energy absorbed by a medium. If an air cavity is introduced into the medium at a point at which the value of the dose is desired, it is possible to relate the ionisation in the air cavity, caused by the flow of electrons through the cavity, to the energy absorbed by the surrounding medium; this is known as the Bragg-Gray theory. If the correct conditions are met the ionisation can be measured by an ionisation chamber placed in the cavity, and when certain factors are applied to this value the energy absorbed is the result. This is usually measured in terms of the rad (1 rad = 100 ergs per g or 10^{-5} J/g). It is necessary to calibrate the ionisation chamber as the various materials used for the electrode and chamber walls produce slightly different numbers of electrons from the medium itself. This calibration can be carried out at the National Physics Standard Laboratory (N.P.L.).

Calorimetry
Another method of measuring an absorbed dose is that of calorimetry. Ionising radiations, however, provide only a very small heating effect of an absorbing medium. The temperature rise produced by even a few thousand rads is less than 1°C. This rise in temperature is so small that very sensitive methods are required to measure the locally absorbed energy. Semiconductor devices, known as thermistors, show a large change in resistance with temperature change; by using a carefully designed Wheatstone bridge this change in resistance may be measured with high accuracy.

Ferrous Sulphate Dosimetry
The oxidation of ferrous sulphate to ferric sulphate by radiation provides an absolute measurement of absorbed dose. If the number of ferric ions produced by a given amount of radiation is known, the amount of ferric sulphate produced by radiation can be measured using an ultra-violet absorption spectrometer and the unknown absorbed dose calculated. Neither this method of dosimetry nor calorimetry are very suitable methods for routine absorbed dose measurements.

Measurement of Isodose Curves
Although there is published data of depth dose for radiotherapy machines it is desirable to measure the isodose curves for a particular machine. This is usually done with an ionisation chamber in a large tank of water, as water has a very similar composition to soft tissue. For superficial and medium energy machines the depth doses are related to the dose at the surface, at megavoltage energy the maximum dose occurs below the surface due to the build-up effect. A simple method of forming isodose curves is to measure doses on a matrix of points and to interpolate to find the 10% levels. A more elegant method is to set the chamber at the correct depth of a 10% level on the central axis determined previously; then, as the chamber is driven laterally, any change in ionisation current is used to automatically drive the chamber to the correct depth to retain the correct isodose level (a servo system). The path of the chamber is automatically plotted to give a complete isodose curve directly.

Build-Up Effect and Measurement

When high-energy photons interact with matter they produce electrons that travel predominantly in the forward direction, whereas with lower-energy photons the electrons produced travel in all directions. Since the dose at a point depends on the number of ions produced in the immediate vicinity and since there are more ions produced at the end of an electron path, the maximum dose for high-energy radiations is not attained until a depth similar to the electron range is reached—e.g. 0.5 cm for cobalt-60 and 2 cm for 8 MV X-rays—thus sparing the skin. Over these small distances the usual thimble chamber has too large a diameter for accuracy of measurement, so thin, flat, ionisation chambers are used to which thin layers of absorbing material can be added (see fig. 3-29).

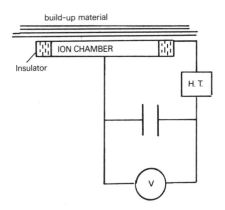

Fig. 3.29. A flat ionisation chamber for measurement in the build-up region of high energy radiation.

Output Measurements

With X-ray sets, where a timer is used, the dose rate for each energy must be determined; where a monitor chamber is used the monitor calibration must be checked to ensure that the correct dose is delivered; on cobalt-60 sets the dose rate is determined when a new source is installed and corrected for decay from month to month. For all these measurements a thimble chamber is used that has been calibrated at the N.P.L. For high energy radiation it is desirable to measure the dose at

5 cm depth in a water phantom. If the percentage depth dose at 5 cm is P, the dose at a 100% is given by:

$$D = R \cdot N \cdot F \cdot \frac{100}{P} \text{ rads,}$$

where R is the instrument reading corrected for atmospheric pressure and temperature; N is the calibration factor and F is the conversion factor to change the ionisation measurement to absorbed dose for the energy used.

CHAPTER 4

Radioisotopes in Radiotherapy

Radium Needles and Tubes

The first radium for medical use was loaned by the Curies. At first tubes of 25-50 mg were buried in growths, needles containing only a few mg came into use in 1910. The best use of needles to obtain reasonably uniform dose distributions was developed by Paterson and Parker at Manchester in 1934. Both tubes and needles are still widely used in radiotherapy to give a high local dose of radiation; though radioactive caesium is replacing radium in many centres.

A radium tube is shown in fig. 4-1. Most radium tubes are 2 cm long and contain 10-50 mg of radium salt. The iridio-platinum

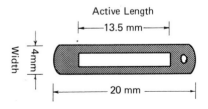

Fig. 4.1. A radium tube.

case absorbs the alpha and beta radiation emitted from radium as these are of no benefit in the treatment. Platinum is suitable as its high density means that the wall of the tube need not be too thick; platinum also has a high atomic number, which means that it absorbs the low-energy gamma rays which would only increase the dose in the tissue immediately surrounding the needle. Tubes are used for intracavity therapy of which the most common treatment is that for carcinoma of the uterine cervix. The radium tubes are placed in standard arrangements within the central canal of the uterus and across the vaginal vault up against the cervix. Various systems for holding the

68

tubes in position have been developed. In the Manchester system the vaginal radium is contained in two rubber ovoids with a choice of spacer between them depending on the individual patient; the uterine radium is contained in a metal tube. There is a choice of central tubes to allow 2, 3 or 4 radium tubes to be placed end to end, depending on the length of the uterine canal. This arrangement gives a high dose to the required volume, the dose to the rectum is reduced by packing with material behind the ovoids.

The insertion of the radium is performed under general anaesthetic. Radiographs are taken to determine the position of the radium; the tubes are easily seen because of their opacity and the cervix can be located by the lower end of the central tube, the rectum is located by a rectal probe opaque to X-rays. The physicist can then calculate the dose at required points by adding the contributions from each source. This can also be done using a computer, but this still usually requires the entering of the coordinate data from the radiographs.

Needles

Radium needles are of the appearance shown in fig. 4-2. They are of smaller diameter than the tubes and have a sharpened end to allow them to be inserted into tissue. The length of a needle

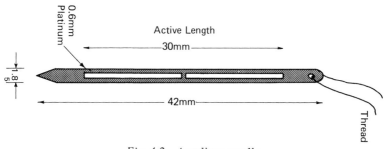

Fig. 4.2. A radium needle.

does not necessarily determine its activity; they are made up from cells of radium salt of differing linear activity. The length of the needle containing the active radium is called the active length; the total length of the needle is about a centimetre more than the active length. Some examples of the loading of radium needles are given in the table:

Designation	Activity	Loading	Active length	Total length	Activity/length of cell
A1	1 mg	a	15 mm	25 mm	$a = 0.5$ mg/15 mm
B2	2 mg	b b	30 mm	42 mm	$b = 1$ mg/15 mm
D2	2 mg	f a a f	45 mm	58 mm	$f = 0.5$ mg/7.5 mm

Radium needles are inserted directly into tissue so that they can give a very high dose of radiation to a malignant growth. Tissues even only 5 cm from the needles will receive only about 1/100 of the dose that points close to the needles receive. It is possible to combine needles in patterns according to rules (Paterson and Parker) so that the combined isodose distribution is one which produces a relatively uniform dose over the tumour volume. A planar implant of the form shown in fig. 4-3

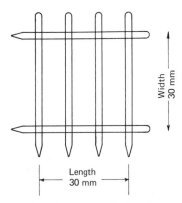

Width 30 mm

Length 30 mm

Fig. 4.3. A needle implant.

will produce a uniform isodose surface ($\pm 10\%$) at $\frac{1}{2}$ cm from the plane of the needles; it is at this distance that the dose is usually specified as at closer distances the isodose curves are irregular in shape.

Performing an Implant
On the basis of his examination of the patient, the therapist decides what needles he will need and their approximate

arrangement from the size and shape of the tumour. These needles will be prepared and sterilised and placed in a lead-lined container in the theatre. They are left in this container until the therapist requests them, when they are removed with long-handled forceps. The needles are inserted in the tumour using short forceps and a pusher so that the therapist need not touch the needles with his fingers. Radiographs are then taken to determine the exact arrangement of the needles from which the physicist can calculate the time for which they must remain in the patient to give the required dose. At the end of the treatment the needles are removed using the attached threads. The needles are then cleaned, checked for damage and placed back in the radium safe. When many needles are used there is the risk of losing one as they are quite small; great care must be taken at all times to ensure that all the needles are accounted for.

Radioactive Caesium
Although radium is a valuable source of radiation, especially since it is virtually everlasting (half-life 1,600 years), it has a number of disadvantages, so that now caesium-137 is available it is replacing radium. The particular advantage of caesium is that it eases shielding problems. The gamma-ray spectrum of radium covers a wide range, up to 2.46 MeV (due to the decay products which cannot escape), whereas caesium-137 only has one gamma-ray energy of 660 keV. This means that, although they have approximately the same isodose curves close to the sources (since the inverse square law accounts for most of the fall-off in dose rate), their half-value layers in protection materials differ by about a factor of two. Not only does this mean that shielding for storage purposes need be much less, but also shielding within the patient, e.g. the rectum in the treatment of the uterine cervix, becomes practical. A second advantage of caesium is that the sources can be smaller than radium sources because of its higher specific activity. This makes it possible to construct a flexible source train for afterloading.

Afterloading technique
When active sources need to be manipulated in the theatre all the staff, but particularly the therapist, receive a small amount of radiation. This is well within the levels allowed by the code of practice, but attempts must continually be made to reduce

the radiation received by staff. One method of doing this is the system of afterloading the radioactive sources. This is practicable with caesium sources for treatment of the uterine cervix. A special applicator, made of perspex (fig. 4-4), is placed in position in the vagina under anae'sthetic. Non-active replicas of

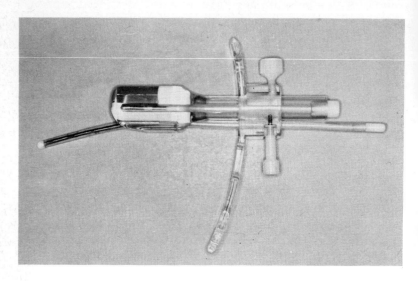

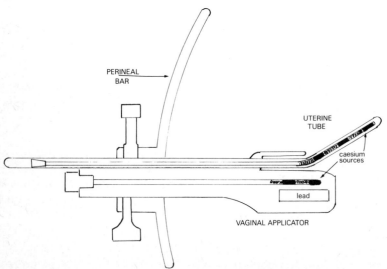

Fig. 4.4. An after-loading device for carcinoma of the cervix constructed from perspex. (Developed at Newcastle R.V.I.)

the source trains (dummy sources) are introduced and the patient radiographed to check their position. The patient then returns to the ward. The active sources can then rapidly be placed in the applicator at the therapist's convenience. The applicator is designed for easy removal and insertion of the source trains, without needing anaesthetic, so that they can be removed for nursing operations and replaced without needing to check the position of the sources by radiography.

Surface Applicators

Radium tubes and their caesium substitutes are mounted at distances of 1-2 cm from the surface of a tumour to provide a form of external superficial therapy with a rapid fall-off in depth dose (see fig. 4-5). The applicator can be moulded from plastic materials, e.g. Bexoid, in the same way as a head mould is produced for high energy beam therapy; a plaster bandage impression is made of the tumour region, a plaster cast replica of that part of the patient can then be made on to which the bexoid can be moulded. The radium is then mounted in grooves cut in the bexoid at regular intervals, with spacing between the ends of the sources no greater than the treatment distance to obtain a uniform dose distribution at the surface to

Fig. 4.5. A surface applicator.

be treated. It is usual for such applicators to be worn for up to 8 hr a day for 5-7 days. For other radio-isotopes for therapy see Table 4-1.

TABLE 4-1

Radioactive nuclides used in radiotherapy

Name	Radiation	Half-life	Form and use
Radium-226	Gammas: 0.19-2.43 MeV	1,620 Y	Needles and tubes 0.5-50 mg
Caesium-137	0.66	30 Y	Needles tubes and seeds 0.5-200 mCi
Cobalt-60	1.17, 1.33	5.3 Y	Intracavity tubes and beads up to 6 Ci Discs for teletherapy up to 5,000 Ci
Tantalum-182	0.07-1.28	115 D	Interstitial wire and hairpins
Gold-198	0.41	2.7 D	Gold grains for volume implantation
Yttrium-90	β's	64 H	Rods, or pellets for pituitary implants
Iodine-131	β's	8 D	As iodide in solution for thyrotoxicosis 5 mCi
Gold-198	β's	65 H	Sterile colloid for treatment of pleural or peritoneal cavity
Strontium-90	β's	28.5 Y	External beta applicator, e.g. for eye 10 mCi

Gold Grains

Radioactive gold (Au-198) with a half life of 2.7 days is used for permanent implantation into tumours. The grains are short lengths of gold wire with a platinum sheath to absorb the beta particles making their overall dimensions about 2.5 x 0.75 mm. They are introduced into tissue using a sterile gold-grain gun (fig. 4-6), which can place the grain at exactly the right position and depth. They are particularly useful for bladder implants and small volume implants of awkward sites. The activity required must be carefully calculated: this can be done using the same Paterson-Parker tables that are used for radium, but changing the formula so that mg-hours (amount of radium used x treatment time) becomes: equivalent mg-hrs = (ratio of k factors x milli-curies destroyed x effective treatment time),

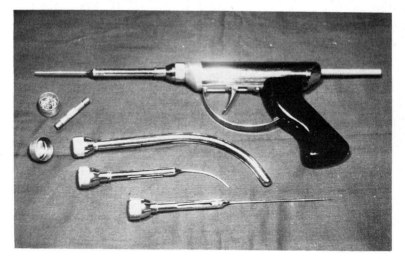

Fig. 4.6. A gold grain gun.

where the effective treatment time is the mean life of Au-198, i.e. 2.7/0.693 days. The ratio of the k factors (see below) must also be taken into account in the calculation. In this case the ratio is 2.3/8.3 for k-gold-198/k-radium. Any isotope that is to be permanently placed in the body can have its total dose calculated in this way. The activity of gold grains is usually 1-2 mCi; this must be specified for a time close to that when the grains will be inserted because of the short life of Au-198.

Intracavity Treatment using Gold Colloid

A second use of radioactive gold uses the beta particles emitted to treat the large surface areas of the peritoneal or pleural cavities without producing a high whole-body dose. Normally the organs of the body fill these cavities, but if the surface becomes involved with a malignancy there may be leakage of fluid into the cavity. This effusion is drained off and replaced with a solution containing colloidal Au-198. The procedure is carried out in the theatre with full aseptic precautions. The fluid is removed through a hollow cannula inserted through the abdominal or chest wall. The cavity is then flushed with saline before allowing the radioactive gold to enter under gravity feed. For the peritoneal cavity activities of 100-200 mCi are used; for the pleural cavities 75-100 mCi are given.

The Use of Phosphorus-32 (^{32}P)

Radioactive phosphorus is a pure beta emitter, and would be ideal for specific-organ radiotherapy. Unfortunately although it tends to be concentrated in cancerous tissue the concentration is seldom high enough to be of practical value. The most useful application is in the treatment of polycythemia. The radioactive phosphorus is taken up by blood-forming bone and destroys a proportion of the red cells so restoring the whole blood to near normal in a few months. A typical activity used would be 5-7 mCi. This is given intravenously.

Radioactive Yttrium (^{90}Y)

This is another beta emitter, with a half-life of 2.5 days. One of the more common uses is in the treatment of the pituitary gland to abolish its secretory activity in hormonal control of breast cancer, or diabetes. The yttrium is formed into the desired shape, rods or pellets, and then activated in a nuclear reactor before insertion.

Radioactive Strontium (^{90}Sr)

This is the parent isotope of yttrium and has a half-life of 28 years. It is used as an external irradiator of the body in two particular instances:

(1) Whole skin irradiation of the body for treatment of mycosisfungoides,
(2) in an eye applicator for treatment of various disorders of the eye.

For the whole skin irradiation a source of several hundred curies is housed in a shield at some distance from the patient to obtain a wide field. The patient is automatically moved under the beam on a motorised table. For eye disorders the eye applicator is of a shape to fit the eyeball; it is made of plastic with strontium foil mounted at a depth of 0.5 mm from the concave face and backed by silver foil to reduce the intensity to the handler (fig. 4-7). The surface dose rate is about 2 rads per sec; treatment to a few hundred rads takes a few minutes and this is repeated weekly for 4-5 weeks for non-malignant conditions such as corneal ulcers; small neoplasms—e.g. melanoma—can be given doses of the order of 15,000 rads in 5-6 weeks.

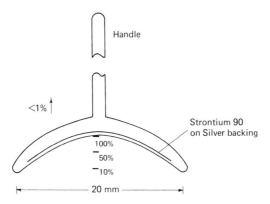

Fig. 4.7. An eye applicator. The radiation through the back of the applicator is less than 1% of that at the anterior surface.

Tantalum wire (^{182}Ta)

The wire is sheathed in platinum to absorb the beta particles. It is used as a substitute for radium especially in sites inconvenient for radium as it can be formed into any desired shape. In the treatment of bladder cancer it can be used in hairpin loops which are inserted into the bladder wall during surgery. Threads attached to the loops are drawn down through a urethral catheter so that at the end of treatment the tantalum loops can be withdrawn without further surgery.

Radioactive iodine (^{131}I)

Radioactive iodine in solution is given for the treatment of thyrotoxicosis. This makes use of the concentration of iodine in the thyroid to give the gland a high dose of radiation from the beta particles. Activities of 5-7 mCi are given depending on the size of the gland and the percentage of the iodine taken up by the gland; this uptake is measured, using the gamma rays and external counter with a tracer quantity of iodine, before the therapy dose is given. Radioactive iodine is also used in the treatment of some thyroid cancers and the metastases from such cancer. In this case doses of the order of 100 mCi are given; this produces a dose to the thyroid of several hundred thousand rads, again depending on the uptake of the gland. A large whole-body dose is also given especially if the uptake in the gland is low. To prevent severe reaction, single doses of no more than 200 mCi should be given.

Dose Calculations for Radio-Isotope Therapy

There are two distinct groups of calculation depending on the type of source: (1) sealed sources for interstitial and intracavity therapy, in which only the gamma rays contribute to the dose as the beta particles are absorbed by the wall materials; (2) internally administered radio-isotopes from which the largest contribution to the dose is from the beta particles.

Sealed Sources

The dose at any point surrounding a gamma ray source can be calculated, knowing the activity of the source, if the *specific gamma ray constant* for the isotope is known. This quantity is known as the k-factor. It is defined as: the exposure rate at 1 cm from a point source having an activity of 1 mCi. A few k-factors of commonly used isotopes are given below:

	k-factor	
Radium-226	8.3	$R \cdot cm^2 \cdot hr^{-1} \cdot mCi^{-1}$
Caesium-137	3.3	
Cobalt-60	13.5	
Gold-198	2.3	
Iodine-131	2.2	

The k-factor can be used to calculate the dose at any point from a point source (fig. 4-8); this can be very useful in protection problems as the distances are usually large enough so

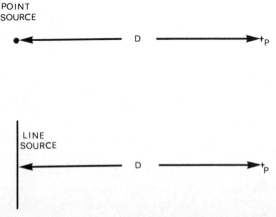

Fig. 4.8. *The exposure rate from a point source is $(k \cdot mCi)/D^2$; from a line source is $(k \cdot mCi)/D^2_{eff}$ $(D < D_{eff})$.*

that any source can be regarded as a point source. However, in general, because the sealed sources are in the form of tubes, needles, wire, etc. the dose calculations become more complex. At a certain distance from the source (at distances greater than twice the largest dimension of the source) it is possible to assume the source to be a point, to obtain a result for the dose rate to within a few per cent. At these distances the inverse square law may be used in conjunction with the k-factor and the activity, A mCi, to calculate the dose at a point from the equation:

$$\text{exposure dose rate,} \qquad X = \frac{kA}{d^2} \, R/\text{hr},$$

where d is the distance in cm from the source.

For precise calculation of the dose rate at a point, the source size must be taken into account and also the intensity change with angle as the radiation passes through different quantities of wall material (the polar diagram). Thus a dose rate at any point in air may be calculated. To calculate the absorbed dose rate in tissue the exposure dose rate must be multiplied by: (i) a correction factor for the absorption and scatter produced in the medium (which for small distances almost cancel each other), and (ii) the correction factor that transforms roentgens to rads (f). This latter factor is 0.965 for most high-energy gamma-emitting radio-isotopes. If there is no decay of activity the total dose is given by:

$$D = \frac{kAt(f)}{d^2} \, \text{rads},$$

where t is the treatment time in hr. For radium the quantity $A \cdot t$ is in mg $\cdot$ hr, more generally it is in mCi $\cdot$ hr.

There is virtually no decay with radium ($T_{1/2} = 1,600$ years), and with caesium the treatment times are short compared with the half-life so that correction to the activity need only be made every 6 months. If the treatment time is short or comparable to the half-life of the isotope allowance must be made for the decay by determining the number of millicuries destroyed in the treatment time. In the case of permanently implanted isotopes this must be the actual amount of activity used, and the time factor used to calculate the dose must be the mean-life of the isotope, i.e.

$$D = \frac{k \cdot \text{mCi}d \cdot (\text{mean-life})(f)}{d^2} \, \text{rads}.$$

If the isotope is removed from the patient the difference between the initial and final activities must be used in the above equation.

Unsealed Sources

The calculation of the beta-ray dose to a given volume is quite different. The beta rays are almost all completely absorbed within the treated volume, thus the dose can be calculated directly from the amount of energy each beta particle contributes to the total absorbed dose. The total number of beta particles emitted per second is given from the activity. Thus the energy available in one second from A mCi of isotope is:

$$A \times 3.7 \times 10^7 \times \bar{E} \text{ MeV}$$

if $\bar{E}$ is the effective beta particle energy in MeV.

If the mass of the organ in which this activity is uniformly distributed is M grams, the absorbed dose per second is:

$$\frac{A \times 3.7 \times 10^7 \times \bar{E} \times 1.6 \times 10^{-13}}{M} \text{ Joules/gram}^{-1}\text{sec}^{-1}$$

or since 1 rad = 10^{-5} J/g, absorbed dose rate = $(0.59\ A \cdot \bar{E})/M$ rad/sec.

For example: if M = 25 grams, A = 5 mCi iodine-131 and $\bar{E}$ = 0.2 MeV, the dose rate to the thyroid gland will be about 0.0236 rads/sec. Now the effective treatment time is a combination of the physical and biological half-lives. This combined half-life is determined by measuring the uptake every day for a few days. If this is found to be 5 days, the effective treatment time is 5/0.693 days and the total dose is then about 150,000 rad.

CHAPTER 5

X-Rays for Diagnostic Use

X-Rays for diagnostic use are produced when a stream of electrons accelerated through a potential difference of 20-120 kV strike a target. The X-rays have a continuous spectrum of energies, with the maximum energy equal to the maximum kilovoltage, due to bremsstrahlung or braking radiation; super-imposed on this is the characteristic radiation specific to the target material (fig. 5-1). The electrons are produced from a

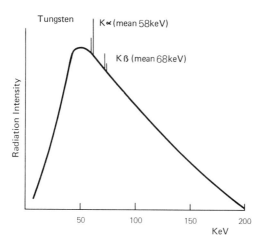

Fig. 5.1. The continuous (bremsstrahlung) X-ray spectrum from a tung-sten target at 200 kV potential showing the K characteristic lines of tungsten.

tungsten filament by thermionic emission. They are accelerated in the vacuum of the tube by the electric field force between the electrodes, then strike the tungsten target. The X-rays are emitted in all directions from the target; only a collimated beam is allowed to escape from the tube head and is directed through the part of the body to be radiographed to strike a film.

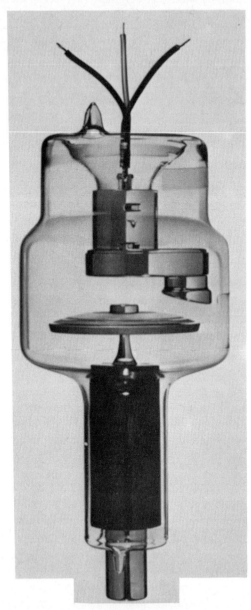

Fig. 5.2. (a) A diagnostic X-ray tube with rotating anode (Courtesy Siemens).

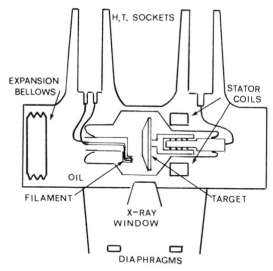

Fig. 5.2. (b) A diagnostic X-ray tube with rotating anode.

THE X-RAY TUBE

The essentials of the diagnostic X-ray tube are shown in fig. 5-2 (a, b). The filament is a coil of tungsten wire $\frac{1}{2}$-1 mm diameter and about 1 cm long. The electric fields acting on the electrons are such as to have a focusing effect to produce a target area at the tungsten anode of about 2 x 6 mm; the target surface is inclined at 17° which produces an effective target area viewed along the X-ray beam of about 2 x 2 mm. In the majority of X-ray tubes the target is tungsten; X-ray tubes for mammography sometimes have molybdenum targets which produce a greater proportion of radiation of useful energy to increase contrast.

The Heat Produced

The bremsstrahlung process only accounts for about 1% of the electrons absorbed, the other 99% of the energy contained in the electron beam produces heat when absorbed by the target. Thus at 100 kV and 100 mA the energy transformed into heat is 9.9 joules in about 0.1 sec (about 1 kW). To avoid damaging the target it must have a high melting point (tungsten melts at 3,380°C) and the heat must be removed from the bombarded area quickly.

To increase the bombarded area the anode can be rotated at high speed (about 3,000 r.p.m.) to spread the heat over an annular path of an area about 100 times that of the stationary target (see fig. 5-3). With the short exposures used in radiography there is not time for the anode to reach full speed before the exposure is completed; a second or two is allowed in the initial switching before an exposure can be made. The heat in the target is dissipated by radiation through the vacuum of the tube into the glass wall and surrounding oil, from where it transfers by convection into the surrounding air.

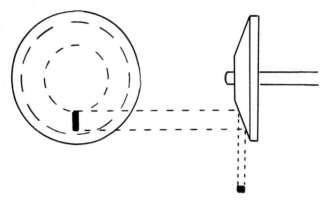

Fig. 5.3. The annular path of the target of the anode showing how the area of bombardment is increased from 12 mm² for a stationary target to about 1000 mm² for rotating target decreasing the watts/cm² by a factor of 80.

In a stationary target X-ray tube the heat conducts along the stem of the anode into cooling fins which are surrounded by cooling oil.

X-RAY GENERATOR AND CONTROL

Voltage Rectification

The power needed to generate X-rays for radiography necessitates the use of the alternating current mains supply. Although the X-ray tube itself acts as a rectifier, and this is made use of in low-power portable X-ray units, a simple means of half-wave rectification is illustrated in the circuit in fig. 5-4 which produces a current wave form in the X-ray tube as shown. Full-wave rectification can be obtained from the circuit shown in fig. 5-5. If the three phases of the mains supply are used a virtually constant voltage is obtained at the output.

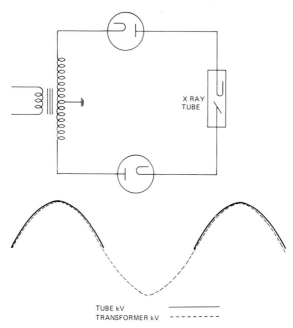

TUBE kV
TRANSFORMER kV   - - - - - - - -

Fig. 5.4. A half-wave rectified X-ray generator showing tube and transformer waveforms.

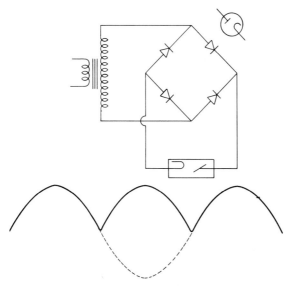

Fig. 5.5. A full wave rectified X-ray generator showing position of rectifiers which may be solid state or valves.

Control of kV, mA, Time

The kilovoltage to be applied to the X-ray tube can be varied in steps of 10 kV by altering a tap on the autotransformer (see fig. 5-6). The tube current is controlled by altering the current

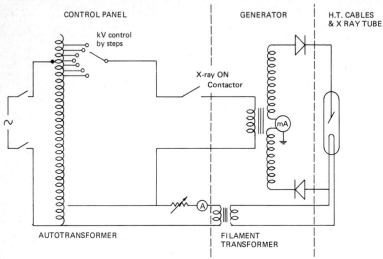

Fig. 5.6. *A simplified complete X-ray generator and control circuit.*

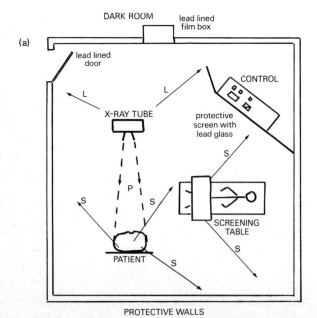

Fig. 5.7(a)

through the filament which changes its level of thermionic emission of electrons. The exposure time can be preset between 0.001 and several seconds. To obtain good reproducibility of timing at very short times electronic timers are used which require no moving parts. The basis of these is the charging of a capacitor through a resistor until a certain voltage is reached which triggers the electronic switch. This switch is a device (e.g. transistor) that conducts only when a signal greater than a certain voltage is applied to one of its electrodes; it is this change of state which operates a relay that switches the X-rays off. All these controls are on a panel located at some distance from the X-ray tube (see fig. 5-7) behind a protective screen so that the radiographer can operate them without receiving any radiation. If it is necessary for the radiographer to be near the

(b)

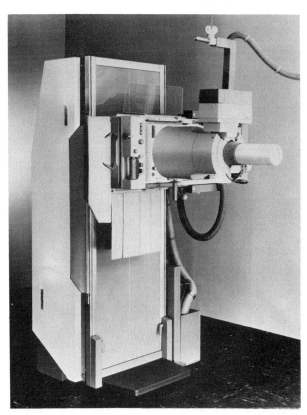

Fig. 5.7. (a) A plan of room showing chest X-ray stand and screening table. (b) A screening unit with table vertical showing image intensifier (Courtesy Philips, Diagnost 62).

patient the controls can be pre-set and the switching operated by hand control. In this case the radiographer wears a lead-rubber apron to absorb any radiation scattered from the patient.

THE PROPERTIES OF X-RAYS IN RADIOGRAPHY

X-Rays produced for diagnostic energy have a spectrum of energies (see fig. 5-1), with maximum energy equal to the maximum kV generated (kVp). The glass window in the X-ray tube provides initial filtration of the very low energies; there is usually also an aluminium filter of 1-2 mm thickness to absorb X-rays that would be absorbed in the surface layers of the patient and thus only increase the skin dose.

X-Rays in this energy range interact with the body tissues by photoelectric absorption and Compton scattering. The radiographic image consists of areas of differing shades of grey because different tissues absorb different quantities of radiation. For example, for X-rays generated at 60 kVp the attenuation of the intensity in 1 cm of bone is about 10 times the attenuation in 1 cm of soft tissue.

THE X-RAY IMAGE

X-Rays have served medicine as a very valuable diagnostic tool since the beginning of the century. During this time the X-ray machines and ancillary equipment have improved in terms of precision and automation, but the basic methods of producing an image of the information in the transmitted X-ray beam have not changed significantly. These are X-ray film and fluoroscopy. There is also the process of Xeroradiography (see below) that is playing an important part in X-ray diagnosis especially in mammography.

X-Ray Film

There is no difference in the basic properties of X-ray film and ordinary light-sensitive film. They both consist of a transparent plastic base material coated with a radiation-sensitive emulsion. This emulsion contains a suspension of minute silver bromide crystals embedded in gelatin.

Image Formation

Where radiation falls on the emulsion of the film a few silver bromide molecules in each grain are reduced to silver. (If a very large amount of radiation is given sufficient metallic silver is produced to show as a discoloration of the film. This needs many times the amount of radiation used to produce an image by the usual processes.) The few silver atoms in each grain act as catalysts when the film is placed in developer, so that most of the silver bromide grain is reduced to silver. Light is absorbed strongly in regions of the film containing silver grains producing regions of blackness; where a smaller amount of radiation has fallen the film is grey, in parts where no radiation has reached the X-ray film remains almost transparent.

It is necessary to remove the underdeveloped silver bromide from the film as this would slowly blacken when exposed to light. This is done by dissolving the silver bromide in sodium thiosulphite ("fixer") which also hardens the gelatin of the emulsion. The film is then washed to remove all residual chemicals, as these would form streaks across the film when dry. The complete process is illustrated in fig. 5-8.

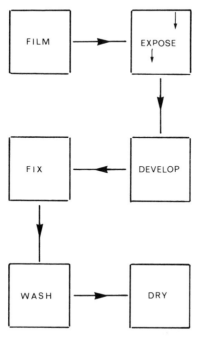

Fig. 5.8. The processing of X-ray film.

The Measurement of Blackness

The human eye is very sensitive to different shades of grey and can discern detail from a radiograph accurately. The physiological response of the eye is logarithmic, so if quantitative measurements of amount of blackness on a film are required they should agree with this response. The measurement used is the optical density of the film defined by $D = \log_{10} I_0/I$ where I_0 = incident light intensity and I = transmitted light intensity,

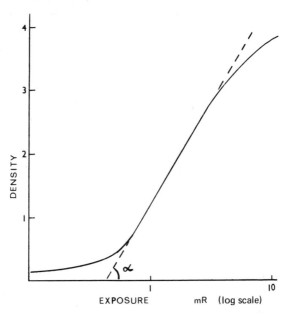

Fig. 5.9. *A graph of film density against exposure.*
$\gamma = tan\ \alpha$

so that for a density of 1 the fraction transmitted is 1/10, and for a density of 2 the fraction transmitted is 1/100. For densities less than 2 in most radiographic film the density is proportional to the amount of radiation reaching the film (expressed in terms of exposure in mR), as shown in fig. 5-9. If the exposure is plotted on a log scale to extend its range, a distinct S-shaped curve, called the characteristic curve of the film, is obtained. The slope of the straight line portion of this curve is known as the film "gamma" (γ). This is a measure of the speed of the film; a fast film has a large gamma.

Intensifying Screens

To effectively increase the speed of a film, and so reduce the amount of radiation needed, intensifying screens are used. These consist of thin layers of high-atomic-number phosphor coated on a base material. The intensifying action of the screen arises because it absorbs more of the X-rays than film and produces a large number of light photons to blacken the film. A common material for a screen is calcium tungstate which has an amplification effect of about 30; thus instead of giving 300 mR to the patient's skin the dose can be reduced to 10 mR. The light emitted from this screen is of a wavelength corresponding to the colour violet, which corresponds to the maximum range of sensitivity of film to light.

Contrast

The contrast in radiography is the difference between optical density of two regions of film: $C = D_1 - D_2$. Thus the contrast between a lung field with a density of 2 and a region of bone shadow of density 0.5 is 1.5. If the soft tissue shows a density of 1 on a radiograph, the lung field will appear twice as black as the soft tissue. Also the contrast between lung/soft tissue will be twice that between soft tissue/bone. When the absorbing materials which produce the density differences are considered it can be shown that the contrast for radiographic film is directly proportional to the difference between the products of attenuation coefficient (μ_1 and μ_2) and thickness (d_1 and d_2), i.e. $C \propto (\mu_1 d_2 - \mu_2 d_2)$. If we take the constant of proportionality as 1.5, the contrast between 2 cm of bone and 10 cm of soft tissue at 60 kVp is: $C = 1.5 (8 \times 2 - 0.8 \times 10)$ which is a large value. However, in practice the contrast is reduced by the overlying layers of tissue and the scatter to the film from the Compton scattering photon interactions.

Natural and Artificial Contrast

A radiograph of the body is an attempt to produce information of a three-dimensional object on a two-dimensional image. The contrast which is produced between two objects is blurred by the other objects through which the X-rays pass. It is possible with practice to diagnose defects in various anatomical sites from radiographs as long as there is sufficient contrast between these sites and the surrounding tissue. Contrasts relative to soft tissue and muscle can be designated as (a) high, e.g. bone and calcific deposits; (b) low, e.g. fatty tissue, (c) very low; e.g. air in the trachea, lung, etc., gas bubbles in G.I. tract. Other parts of the body are difficult to detect accurately on radiographs as they have similar contrast to their surroundings, e.g. body fluids. In this case it is necessary to use artificial means of contrast.

Artificial Contrast Media

One of the more common agents is the barium meal consisting of barium sulphate as an aqueous suspension. This is used to outline the oesphagus, stomach, G.I. tract, etc. The complete path of the barium drink can be followed by fluoroscopy plus a cine film recording or a television plus video tape recording. The stomach is a difficult organ from which to obtain reliable information. It is either too distended or the walls are folded in on themselves, so that any small features, e.g. the tell-tale signs of ulceration, are difficult to see. It has been suggested that a small dose of tonic water is sufficient to achieve just the right amount of distension, i.e. a carbonated barium drink.

Organic compounds containing up to 50% iodine (high atomic number) are used to outline small blood vessels and lymph drainage vessels. Even if a vessel is only 1 mm in diameter it will be almost opaque to X-rays. The techniques using these contrast media are known as: intravenous urography (or pyelography) for study of kidneys, ureters and bladder; angiography—contrast medium introduced into blood vessels or lymph drainage.

Air or gas is also a very useful contrast medium. It can be introduced into the brain ventricles after removal of fluid (ventriculogram). The surfaces of the ventricles can then be studied by changing the orientation of the patient so that the air space takes up a different position within the ventricle.

The Effect of Scattered Radiation on Contrast

The information required in radiography is contained in the primary beam, the attenuation of the beam by different objects produces a pattern of intensity that is recorded on film. An important problem in radiography is that this information can be obscured by scattered radiation. This scatter is at a fairly constant level across the whole film, but the shape of the characteristic curve means that the density does not increase equally over all parts of the film. In the example above suppose that the primary radiation only produces densities as follows:

	Primary dose	Density
Bone:	10 mR	0.5
Lung field:	45 mR	2.0
Contrast: 1.5		
(Gamma: 1.0 approx.)		

If the scatter dose is 10 mR across the film

	Primary and scatter	Density
Bone:	20 mR	1.2
Lung field:	55 mR	2.2
Contrast: 1.0		

Thus the contrast is reduced from 1.5 to 1.0 by the scattered radiation.

Reduction of Scattered Radiation to the Film

It is possible to reduce the actual amount of scattered radiation by: (1) reducing the total volume of tissue in the beam, mainly by reducing the beam size to the size needed to cover the film used. (2) using as low a kilovoltage as possible, since Compton scattering becomes more and more the dominant interaction process as the kilovoltage is increased. However, a sufficiently high kilovoltage must be used to penetrate the part of the body being radiographed.

To reduce the amount of scatter received by the film the most common method is to use a grid of some type over the film. The principle of this is shown in fig. 5-10b. Most scattered radiation is moving at a different angle to the primary radiation, thus the majority of it will be absorbed in the strips of lead. These strips are thin enough to allow many of them to be used without affecting the image unduly. Commonly used grids have between 20 and 30 strips per cm; these strips are about 0.005 cm thick. To prevent the grid pattern being superimposed

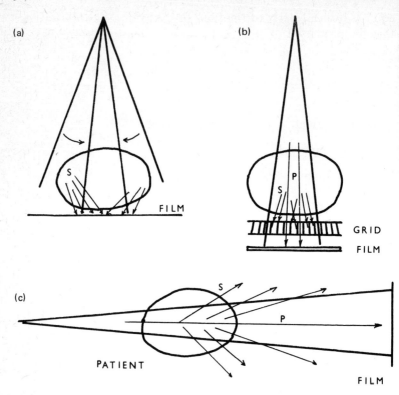

Fig. 5.10. *Showing methods of reducing scattered radiation to film. (a)*
Reducing beam size. (b) Use of a grid. (c) Placing film at a distance. P =
primary radiation. S = scatter.

on the X-ray image the grid can be moved a short distance
during an exposure. The simplest movement consists of a spring
to pull the grid across the beam at uniform speed; the speed is
controlled by an oil dash-pot. The grid is set moving automatically
by the exposure control and the exposure made when it is
moving at the correct speed. It moves a total distance of about
1 inch in a time that can be varied from 0.2 to 15 seconds
depending on the length of time of the exposure.

A second method of reducing the scatter received by the film
is simply to place the film at a distance from the patient (fig.
5-10c) in which case the scatter at anything other than small
angles does not reach the film. This form of radiography is
sometimes used and is known as magnification or detail radio-

graphy. The disadvantage of the technique for all radiography is that the image is magnified, which does not allow a complete picture to be recorded on one film.

The Procedure of Taking a Radiograph
A common radiograph is the P.A. chest. The patient stands with his chest against the cassette which is held on a stand. So that the full lung fields can be seen on the radiograph the shoulders are rotated forward and the patient fully inhales. The radiographer then steps behind a protective screen and takes an exposure at standard settings, e.g. 70 kVp, 10 mAs.

The Interpretation of the Radiograph
As mentioned above the X-ray image is a two-dimensional display of a three-dimensional object, thus parts of the body are superimposed on each other. X-rays travel in straight lines, forming a diverging beam from the focus so that all objects are magnified, and objects further away from the film are more greatly magnified than objects close to the film (see fig. 5-11). This can be seen in a chest radiograph in which the posterior ribs can be seen to be wider than the anterior. The magnification of a particular object within the body can only be obtained if all the measurements shown on the figure are known.

Focal Spot Size
The finite size of the focal spot produces a certain penumbra depending on the geometry of the source-patient-film system. This is not usually a problem for most diagnoses, but certain precise techniques demand good resolution of detail and specially small focal spots can be used (0.3 x 0.3 mm) for this purpose.

Pin Hole Picture of Focal Spot
To obtain the effective dimensions of the focal point, which is useful if damage to the anode is suspected, a pin hole image of the focus can be made. A very fine hole is made in a sheet of lead 1-2 mm thick. This is placed on the central axis of the beam at a known distance from the focus. A film is placed at an

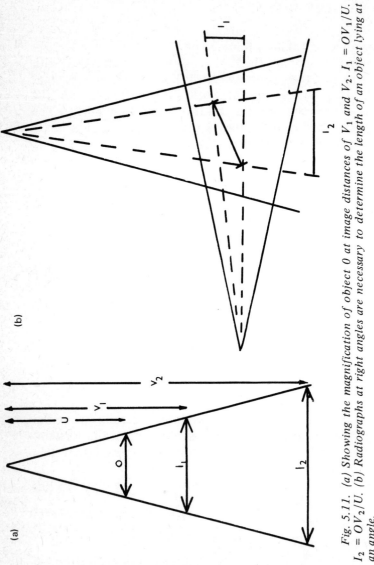

Fig. 5.11. (a) Showing the magnification of object 0 at image distances of V_1 and V_2. $I_1 = OV_1/U$. $I_2 = OV_2/U$. (b) Radiographs at right angles are necessary to determine the length of an object lying at an angle.

$$\text{Length of object} = \left[\left(\frac{I_1}{m_1} \right)^2 + \left(\frac{I_2}{m_2} \right)^2 \right]^{\frac{1}{2}}$$

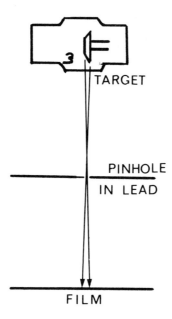

Fig. 5.12. The arrangement for a pin hole photograph of the target.

equal distance from the lead and an exposure made. This geometry produces a real size image of the focus (see fig. 5-12).

FLUOROSCOPY

If the radiologist wishes to view an image of the X-rays passing through a patient so that he can see directly the effects of patient movement, swallowing action, etc. a fluorescent screen is used. The physical action of the fluorescent screen is the same as the intensifying screen described above, i.e. X-rays are converted into flashes of light. A common material for fluorescent screens is zinc cadmium sulphide which produces light of yellow-green colour to which the eye is most sensitive. Caesium iodide is also now used as a phosphor. It is claimed to absorb 2-3 times the radiation that zinc sulphide absorbs, thus producing a brighter initial image. This is partly due to the fact that a thicker layer of phosphor can be used because the crystallites of caesium iodide are aligned and act as light guides.

It is unusual nowadays to view the screen directly as the light level is very low and long periods of dark adaption of the eyes are necessary to perceive detail usefully.

Image Amplification

To overcome these problems image amplification techniques have been developed. The processes most commonly in use are based on the system illustrated in fig. 5-13. The final image

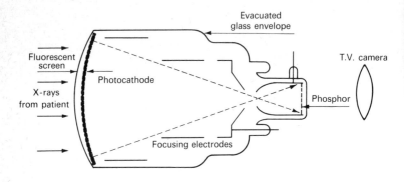

Fig. 5.13. Image intensifier.

which can easily be seen on the viewing screen is formed in the following ways:

1. the photo cathode which is in intimate contact with the fluorescent screen emits electrons with the same intensity pattern as the light image on the fluorescent screen.
2. the electrons are accelerated by a voltage of 25 kV applied between cathode and fluorescent viewing screen, which provides an effective amplification of about 40.
3. the electrons are also focused onto a smaller viewing fluorescent screen which effectively amplifies the image by the ratio:

$$\frac{\text{Area of first (image) fluorescent screen}}{\text{Area of second (objective) fluorescent screen}}$$

since the same electron flux is concentrated onto a smaller area.

Thus the overall amplification is about 1,000 times. Although production of the final image is indirect this system of image intensification is the basis of many commercial products.

Increasing the Field Size

One of the main limitations of this system is that the first fluorescent screen can only be at most 9-12 inches diameter because of the limitations on size of the intensifier. To enable the field size that can be viewed to be increased an optical reducing system is incorporated between a large fluorescent screen and the intensifier (see fig. 5-14). In this system the

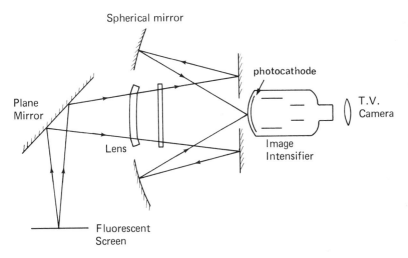

Fig. 5.14. Optical reducing system.

viewing of the image is by television. This is convenient for the radiologist because the television monitor can be placed for him to see while he performs the necessary operations with patient and X-ray machines.

It is possible to reduce the number of stages in obtaining the final image by attaching the first section of the intensifier directly to a television camera. The electronic scanning system of the camera is then used to view the photocathode which is directly excited by the accelerated electrons.

Recording of Images

It is very convenient to be able to view events that have happened quickly at leisure and with the possibility of studying a particular sequence in detail. Video tape recording of the television images makes this possible, although a cine film can also be used to record images directly from the viewing fluorescent screen.

SPECIAL TECHNIQUES IN X-RAY DIAGNOSIS
Neuroradiology

The neuroradiologist needs to use very precise techniques to visualise the tiny capillaries in the brain in his search for defects such as aneurysm. He uses the usual technique of angiography combined with:

1. a fine focal spot X-ray tube (0.3 x 0.3 mm).
2. magnification to obtain good details and to avoid the use of a grid,
3. a subtraction technique to remove the unwanted images of bony structures.

Subtraction Technique (fig. 5-15)

The patient's head is immobilised and a normal magnification radiograph taken. Contrast medium is introduced into the blood vessels of the head and a second radiograph taken. A print of the first radiograph is made (i.e. a positive image); this is superimposed on the second radiograph on a light box to produce an image that shows only the contrast medium in the blood vessels. A contact print can be made of this image.

Xeroradiography (fig. 5-16)

A radiographic technique which has now found merit especially in mammography is that of xeroradiography. This is based on a similar principle to the xerox copying process. The plate that is exposed to radiation is made of metal with a thin layer of selenium on it. This is a semiconductor that passes electric current only in parts that are exposed to X-rays, and this current will depend on the X-ray intensity. If a charge is deposited on the selenium layer before exposure and it is then placed in a non-uniform X-ray beam, the charge will leak away locally to the metal base plate to an extent determined by the X-ray intensity at that point in the beam. The pattern of charge remaining can be visualised by exposing it to a fine cloud of powder of opposite charge. Since charge remains in parts where little radiation has reached, the powder is attracted to these parts, thus displaying the same light and dark pattern as the usual X-ray film. However, xeroradiography has the striking characteristic of high local contrast; the powder is deposited preferentially at boundaries, thus making bone detail, calcifications of a soft tissue structure and skin outline easily visible on the same plate. This makes the technique most suitable for mammography.

Tomography
Generally a radiographic image consists of a jumble of three-dimensional information displayed in two-dimensions. The skilled consultant can sort out from this the information he requires—especially if more than one view through the patient is taken. However, there are methods of obtaining information about the anatomy in a single plane of the patient. This is achieved by various forms of tomography.

Linear Tomography
Perhaps the simplest and most commonly used type of tomography is linear tomography (fig. 5-17). The X-ray target moves along a linear path and the head rotates so that the beam is always directed through a fixed point in the patient. If the film is simultaneously moved so that the shadow of an object at this fixed point always falls at the same spot on the film, the film will record a definite image of the anatomy in one plane only. The shadows from other planes of the body will be blurred by the movement. It is rather like matching speed with a moving object—if you don't the object is just seen as a blur.

It is convenient and desirable from a patient dose point of view that a number of planes are recorded simultaneously using a multicassette box with the films about 1 cm apart. The absorption of the X-rays in the overlying cassettes makes it necessary to use effectively more sensitive film for the lower planes by using faster screens.

Transverse Axial Tomography
The purpose of this type of tomography is to produce an image of the cross-sectional anatomy of the patient. This is especially useful for visualising cross-sections of the skull and cross-sections of the thorax for radiotherapy treatment planning. The beam is angled down through the patient at an angle of 30° to the horizontal to arrive at the film placed horizontally. The

(a)

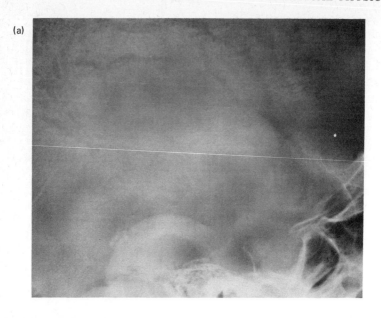

(b)

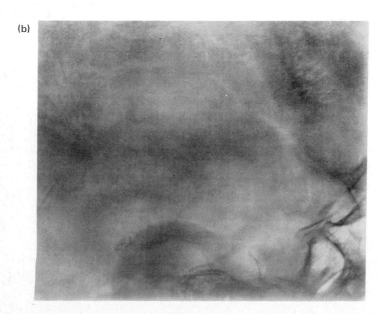

Fig. 5.15a and b.

(c)

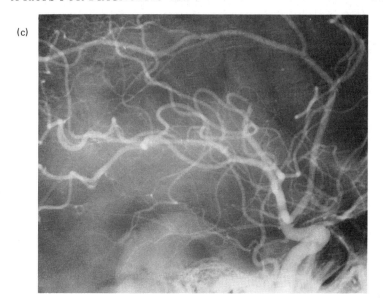

(d)

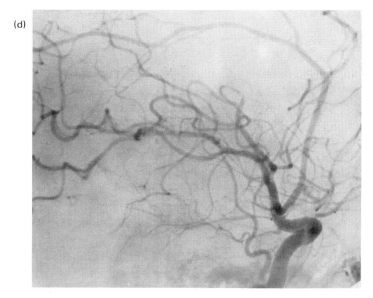

*Fig. 5.15. (a) Direct magnification control film. (b) Diapositive of (a).
(c) Direct magnification arteriogram of cerebral vessels. (d) Subtraction
of (b) from (c).*

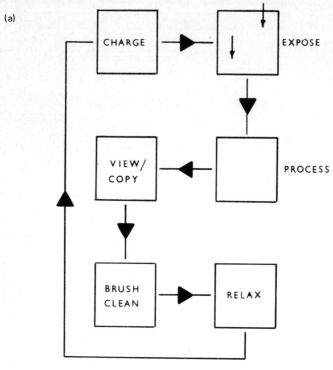

Fig. 5.16(a)

patient and film cassette are rotated through 360° during exposure. The shadows of objects in the horizontal plane in the patient remain effectively stationary on the film as it rotates. Shadows of objects at other levels in the patient are blurred by movement.

A slight variation on this method, which unfortunately introduces very difficult machine construction problems, is to have the patient horizontal and to rotate the X-ray head and film around his long axis. This is very useful for radiotherapy in which the patient is usually in the horizontal position and some organs can change position depending on patient orientation.

Quantitative Tomography

A very recent development uses the principle of film transaxial tomography, but effectively increases the contrast by computer manipulation of data. The X-rays are directed

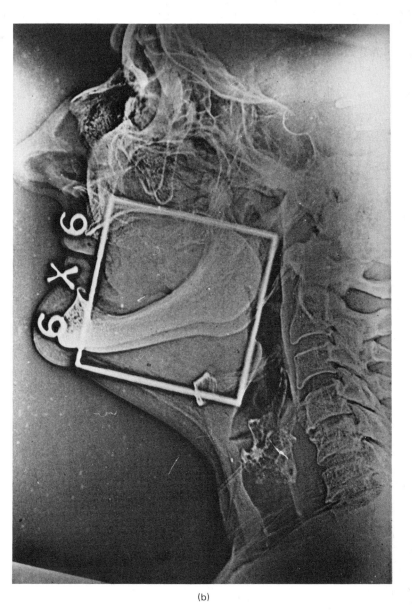

(b)

Fig. 5.16. (a) Block diagram of Xeroradiographic process. (b) A lateral head and neck Xeroradiograph.

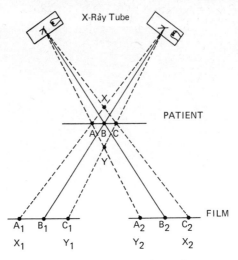

Fig. 5.17. Linear tomography showing how the image of an object X, or Y, outside plane of interest, (A–B–C) moves as film moves.

through the patient and detected by a scintillation counter. To avoid the complication of scatter a very narrow X-ray beam is used and scanned across the usual beam width in conjunction with the detector. The tube and detector are then rotated through 1° and scanning repeated. This is repeated for the full 180°. For tomography of the skull (E.M.I. scanner) 160 transmission measurements are made on each scan. Thus 28,000 (180 x 160) measurements are taken and processed by computer to produce a matrix of 80 x 80 cells with a value of absorption coefficient attributed to each cell. This can be displayed on a screen with a grey scale which corresponds to absorption values. This system greatly assists the diagnosis of brain diseases and disorders such as tumours, cysts and haemorrhages.

QUANTITATIVE MEASUREMENTS USING EXTERNAL X- OR GAMMA-RAY BEAMS

Although ordinary radiography can provide a very useful picture of very fine detail of the inside of the body, it is sometimes valuable to obtain a quantitative measurement of the amount of a certain material in the body. For example: the amount of dust in the lungs; the quantity of bone mineral in a limb; the lung density. An estimate of the quantities can be made from the ordinary radiograph, but the film density is affected by: the quality dependence of the film, its exposure, development, etc., so that even films taken on the same patient will not show the same density in the area of interest. Instead of using film as the detector a scintillation counter can be used to give a direct measurement of the amount of radiation transmitted. Some examples of the use of transmission measurements using X- or gamma-rays are illustrated below.

Lung Function
As inspiration and expiration takes place lung tissue changes in density (between about 0.2-0.4 gm/cm^3 for normal lung tissue). If a narrow gamma-ray beam is directed through the lung, the transmitted radiation varies in intensity with breathing as the total quantity of tissue in the beam changes (the lung expands up-down, i.e. out of the beam, as well as in-out). If recording apparatus is used which is similar to that for the radioisotope renogram a recording of intensity against time is obtained. Normal lung gives a typical intensity trace with time; any abnormality shows as a change in part or all of the trace depending on the severity of the condition.

Dust in the Lung
Many workers in industry suffer from the condition generally described as pneumoconiosis when very fine dust particles (<5 μ) are inhaled and become deposited in the lung. Quantitative measurement of these dusts *in vivo* is complicated by the fact that the amount of dust is very much smaller than the amount of tissue (mg/cm^2 dust compared to g/cm^2 tissue, i.e. $1 : 1,000$). If there is sufficient dust of high atomic number material with respect to tissue (so that it has considerably more absorption, preferably $1,000x$) it is possible to measure the quantity of dust in the lung using a radiation beam of suitable energy that provides sufficient differential between the dust and the tissue, but is not absorbed too much so that the counting statistics are poor. A high energy radiation beam must also be used to measure the quantity of tissue only (at high energy only Compton absorption takes place and the beam does not "see" the dust). There is a special case in which the quantity of dust need only be small, that of antimony oxide. The absorption coefficient of antimony is shown in fig. 5-18. This shows an

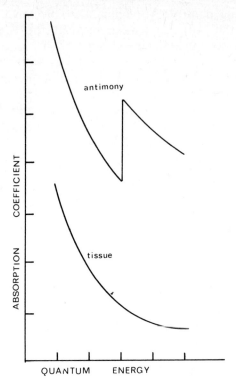

Fig. 5.18. Mass absorption coefficient of antimony compared with water.

abrupt change at the K absorption edge. If beams of X-rays of energy just above and below the absorption edge are used the effect of tissue absorption is eliminated and the large change in absorption coefficient allows milligram quantities of antimony to be measured.

Bone Densitometry
The density of bone is a fairly constant parameter in normal people, but there are various conditions where calcium is not replaced and bone density decreases. Constant monitoring of the whole skeleton is desirable in these patients especially if relatively short term effects of therapy (few months) are to be seen. Ordinary radiography is widely used for this, but quantitative measurements can be made using gamma-rays from an isotope source and a scintillation detector (fig. 5-19). One of the

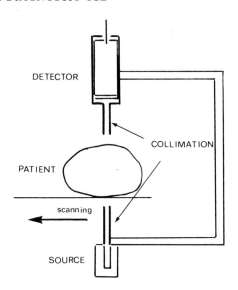

Fig. 5.19. General X-ray scanning apparatus.

bones in a limb is usually used, e.g. metacarpel, radius or femur, across which the measurement is made. A very fine beam of gamma-rays is used which automatically scans across the bone and the transmitted intensity measurement is recorded on a chart recorder or as punched holes in paper tape for a computer. It must be remembered that there is also tissue surrounding the bone. To take this into account the gamma-rays must always pass through a constant thickness of soft tissue. Constant thickness can be achieved by placing the hand in water, if metacarpel is to be measured, or by having the leg in a parallel sided perspex box if the femur is to be measured. The area under the curve [of log (intensity) against distance] is proportional to the total bone in gm/cm of length.

The most useful way of using this measurement is by comparing it with a measurement over exactly the same place on the same patient at subsequent times. Absolute measurement of bone density is very difficult to obtain as the absorption in both must be known accurately by measuring many samples of powdered bone, and the errors of the measuring system must be determined. Providing all parameters stay constant however, comparative measurements can be made with good accuracy, typically ±2%.

CHAPTER 6

The Use of Radioisotopes in Diagnosis

INTRODUCTION

The use of radioisotopes in medicine has increased enormously since about 1960; in both the research and routine use to determine physiological parameters they are making a very useful contribution to diagnosis. This progress has been achieved because of the advances in nuclear physics especially in the subjects of radiation detection and radioisotope production.

PRODUCTION OF RADIOISOTOPES

There are a number of radioactive substances occurring naturally from which pure radioisotopes can be extracted (e.g. radium, uranium). They are, however, mainly high atomic number elements which emit alpha particles and neutrons as well as gamma rays and are therefore of little use in diagnostic work where pure gamma emitters are the ideal isotopes and the more commonly occurring gamma emitter, which also emits beta particles, is acceptable as a tracer.

Radioisotopes can be produced in two distinct ways:

(1) By bombarding a non-radioactive substance with neutrons or charged particles, or protons;
(2) by separating the required isotope from fission products formed in a nuclear reactor (see fig. 6-1).

Neutron Bombardment (i) neutron capture [(n,γ) reactions]
The neutrons produced in the fission reactions in nuclear reactors (see below) are of relatively low energy (slow neutrons of a few eV) and can be captured by the nuclear forces of elements.

The action itself causes a gamma-ray to be emitted, e.g.

$$^{23}_{11}\text{Na} + ^{1}_{0}n \rightarrow ^{24}_{11}\text{Na} + \gamma.$$

110

The sodium atom now has an excess number of neutrons and becomes a radioactive beta-emitter. No new element is formed so purification is not necessary; but this is also a disadvantage as the activity that can be attained in a given volume of sodium is limited, because the radioactive sodium formed decays as fast as neutrons can be pumped in and a saturation level is reached.

(ii) (n,p) Reactions

Fast neutrons can be obtained from proton accelerators (e.g. cyclotron) by bombarding a target with protons. The neutrons have sufficient energy to knock out protons from nuclei and to substitute themselves at the site of the proton, e.g. $^{35}_{17}Cl + ^{1}_{0}n \rightarrow ^{35}_{16}S + ^{1}_{1}p$.

The number of nucleons thus remains constant, but there is an excess of neutrons so that the sulphur becomes a beta emitter. Chemical separation is performed which allows only radioactive atoms of sulphur to be obtained, thus high specific activity (mCi/mg) is possible.

Charged Particle Bombardment

Protons or deuterons or alpha particles can be accelerated in a cyclotron to high energies. If any of these are used to bombard certain elements, they knock neutrons out of the atom to form positron emitters, e.g. $^{52}_{24}Cr + ^{4}_{2}\alpha \rightarrow ^{52}_{26}Fe + ^{1}_{0}n$, as the elements so formed have an excess number of protons.

Fission Products

Nuclear fission is the term used to describe the reaction when a heavy nucleus is caused to disintegrate into two or more roughly equal parts known as fission fragments. Fission takes place when a heavy element, e.g. uranium, is bombarded with neutrons; the neutron combines with the nucleus of uranium to form a highly excited compound nucleus which then disintegrates according to a general equation

$$^{235}_{92}U + n \rightarrow X + Y + pn + \text{energy}$$

where X and Y can be almost any element of medium atomic number, and p extra neutrons are produced. The fission energy ($\sim$200 MeV) released in this reaction is a result of the relatively large real mass difference (as distinct from mass expressed as an integer in terms of nucleons present) between the uranium and the fission products, and mass can be expressed in terms of

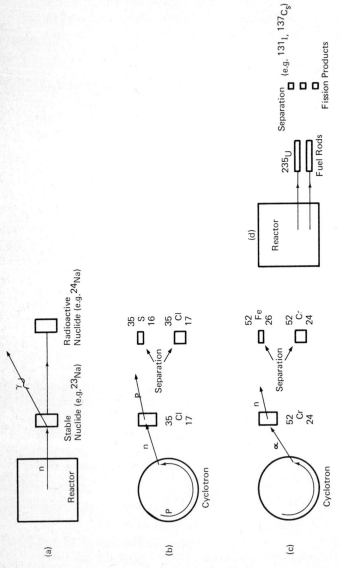

Fig. 6.1. (a) Neutrons from a nuclear reactor are used to irradiate the sample which is placed within a chamber in the reactor. (b) Protons accelerated in a cyclotron interact with the target to produce high energy neutrons which are used to bombard the sample. Since the (n,p) reaction involves a change in atomic number it is possible to separate the radioactive nuclide. (c) Other particles, e.g. alpha particles can be accelerated in a cyclotron and used to bombard the sample. (d) The fission reaction involves the decay of the radioactive fuel, e.g. U-235, into other radioactive nuclides which can be separated from the fuel rods.

energy according to Einstein's equation $E = mc^2$. If the rate of this reaction is controlled, as it is in a nuclear reactor, the release of energy can be used to heat water, to produce steam to provide power to drive a turbine; if the reaction is not controlled it proceeds at enormous speed and the energy is released virtually instantaneously in the form of an explosion.

The fission fragments can be extracted from the original rod of uranium by chemical means. Some of these fission products that are used in medicine are:

Strontium-90	Yttrium-90
Iodine-131	Caesium-137

RADIOPHARMACEUTICALS

The principle of the use of radioisotopes in diagnosis is that very low activities, mainly of the order of 1-1,000 μCi are added to biological compounds to *label* them so that they can then be injected into the patient or given orally and followed through the body in various ways (fig. 6-2). The test is performed either (i) *in vivo*, where the paths or accumulation site of the labelled compound is determined with an external radiation detector, or (ii) *in vitro* in which samples of body fluids (usually blood) are obtained from the patient and the amount of the labelled compound present is determined from the activity in the sample; (iii) there is a third category of test which does not involve giving the patient any radioactivity—analytical tests involving reagents and body fluid samples, e.g. plasma.

LABELLING

A labelled compound has one or more of its atoms substituted by a radioactive atom either of the same atomic number (isotopic labelling) or a different one (non-isotopic labelling), e.g. Hippuran (Iodohippuric acid) labelled with radioactive iodine is isotopically labelled; selenomethionine has a sulphur atom replaced by ^{75}Se atom. The compound to be labelled can be any substance that is non-toxic in the concentration to be used. With new techniques of labelling and the availability of different radioactive isotopes the list of radiopharmaceuticals has increased enormously. The compound and its radioisotope label must be free from toxic impurities, including pyrogens and micro-organisms, which means adhering to rigid sterile technique when preparing and handling the materials. Although most compounds can be sterilised in an autoclave there are

Fig. 6.2. A schematic diagram to show the different forms of tests involving radioactive tracers: (a) in vivo; *(b)* in vitro, *(c) analytical testing of body fluids. Only (a) and (b) involve radiation to the patient.*

exceptions, e.g. human serum albumin (H.S.A.) which must be prepared aseptically; a simple solution to this is to keep the substance in a tube sealed with a special cap which hypodermic needles can puncture many times without producing a leak. Fortunately, as tests have become routine, these compounds can be provided in suitable form already labelled that require a minimum of preparation. The notable exception has been macro-aggregated H.S.A. for lung scanning, but microspheres of this are now available which overcome the problem of preparation and also the difficulty of obtaining a uniform and correct size of macroaggregate.

The Isotopes used for Labelling

An important advantage of radioisotope techniques of diagnosis is that only a very small mass of the isotope is required, usually only of the order of micro-gram quantities. Thus, in general, the labelling substance in a radiopharmaceutical is at a level well below that which will produce a pharmacological response; this may be important if a compound is non-isotopically labelled. However, these very low masses do mean that in some cases (e.g. iodine for iodine uptake tests) a carrier quantity of non-radioactive iodine (^{127}I) must be added to distribute the radioactive atoms throughout the solution to (i) allow the solution to be handled without the possibility of losing all the radioactivity in a fraction of a drop, (ii) to ensure thorough mixing of the radioactive atoms throughout the volume of interest.

In radioisotope diagnostic tests the activity to be measured is either (i) within the body (*in vivo*) in which case the gamma emitters must be used to penetrate the body tissues (the exception is the beta emitter ^{32}P which can be measured in superficial skin or eye tumours), or (ii) in a volume of fluid from the body, when the majority of tests use gamma emitters, but beta emitters may be used with special measuring techniques. To keep the dose to the patient as low as possible there are a number of points to consider:

   (i) the time of elimination of the labelled compound from the body which is measured in terms of biological half life,
  (ii) the half-life of the isotope itself,
 (iii) whether the isotope is a pure gamma emitter. Many gamma emitters are also beta emitters and if the isotope is concentrated in an organ a high local dose will be given from the beta rays, e.g. ^{131}I emits beta particles as well as gammas and is concentrated in the thyroid gland, thus even a few μCi for a tracer test can give 10 rads to the gland. ^{99m}Tc on the other hand can be used in tests in mCi quantities, because it is a pure gamma emitter.

(For calculation of beta-ray dose to an organ see section in chapter on radioisotopes in treatment.)

Some common radionuclides used in diagnosis

Name	Nuclide	Gammas (MeV)	Half-life	Uses
Chlormerodrin	^{197}Hg	0.19 0.077	64H	Brain scanning, 1 mCi Kidney scanning, 200 µCi
Chlormerodrin	^{203}Hg	0.279	47D	Kidney scanning, 200 µCi
Cyanocobalamin (vitamin B_{12})	^{57}Co	0.136 0.122 0.0144	267D	B_{12} absorption with and without I.F., 1 µCi
	^{58}Co	0.81 0.511	71D	
Ferric citrate	^{59}Fe	1.29 1.10 0.19	45D	Iron clearance from plasma, 10 µCi
Gallium citrate	^{67}Ga		78H	Iron absorption studies Tumour localisation, 2 mCi
Indium from sterile generator containing ^{113}Sn ($T_{1/2} = 118$D)	^{113}In	0.393	104M	D.T.P.A.* kidney scan, 5 mCi; D.T.P.A. brain scan, 10 mCi; Chloride, placentography less than 1 mCi
Fibrinogen	^{125}I	0.035 †	60D	Deep vein thrombosis 100 µCi
Sodium iodohippurate	^{131}I	0.72 0.64 0.36 0.28 0.08	8D	Renography 40 µCi

Potassium chloride	^{42}K	1.53	12.4H	Total exchangeable potassium 100 μCi
L-Selenomethionine	^{75}Se	0.097 0.405	120D	Pancreas and parathyroid scanning, 200 μCi. Blood studies
Sodium chloride	^{24}Na	2.75 1.37	15H	Total exchangeable sodium, 50 μCi
Strontium chloride	^{85}Sr	0.514	64D	Bone scanning, 50 μCi Calcium Metabolism, 30 μCi
Strontium 87m from yttrium 87 sterile generator	^{87m}Sr	0.388	2.8H	Bone scanning, 1 mCi
Technetium 99m from molybdenum 99 sterile generator ($T_{1/2}$ = 67H)	^{99m}Te	0.14	6H	Brain scanning, 10 mCi; Lung scanning, 2 mCi (microspheres); Bone scanning, 10 mCi (polyphosphate); Thyroid uptake, 20 mCi
Xenon	^{133}Xe	0.081	5.3D	Lung ventilation studies

* DTPA–Diethylene Triamine Penta acetic acid.

† Also 0.027 keV from Tellurium K X-rays.

For *in vivo* measurements the gamma-ray energy must be sufficiently high to reach the detector from inside the body without too much attenuation; thus ^{125}I, with an energy of 27 keV, is not suitable for *in vivo* measurement because it is attenuated to about 1/30 by 10 cm tissue; however, it is suitable for small volume *in vitro* measurements. Some commonly used radionuclides are given in the table.

Short-Lived Daughters from Isotope "Cows"
Although radioisotopes with short half-lives can be produced in a cyclotron, they must be used almost immediately or they will decay to too low an activity for practical purposes. However, some very suitable isotopes, for diagnostic purposes, are daughter products of longer-lived parents. The basic principle of the isotope cow is that the daughter can be separated "on site" from its parent. Two examples of this type of isotope generator are given below.

Technetium-99m (Half-Life: 6 Hours)
The parent, molybdenum-99, in the form of ammonium molybdate is absorbed onto an alumina column contained in a perspex or glass tube. The daughter is eluted in the form of sodium pertechnetate by passing sterile saline through the column. This must not be done too frequently, about every 6-7 hours, if a reasonable yield of daughter is to be obtained.

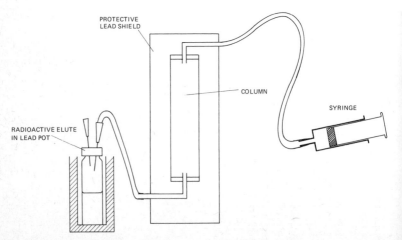

Fig. 6.3. A sterile generator for producing short-lived radioactive nuclides, e.g. technetium-99m.

Technetium-99m is an isomer of technetium-99 in a metastable state which decays to the ground state by emission of a gamma ray only.

Indium-113m (Half-Life: Approximately 2 Hours)
The parent, tin-113m, is absorbed on an ion-exchange material. The daughter is eluted in the form of indium chloride by passing 5-7 ml of 0.04 N hydrochloric acid, elution must be done at not less than 2-hour intervals.

Columns of these radioactive isotopes may contain up to 500 mCi and so are surrounded with lead shielding as shown in fig. 6-3 to reduce the radiation dose.

RADIATION DETECTION EQUIPMENT FOR RADIOISOTOPE DIAGNOSTIC TESTS
The first detectors that were used to measure the quantity of radiation emitted from a patient were ionisation chambers and G.M. tubes. These have a similar construction (fig. 6-4)

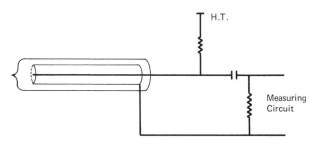

Fig. 6.4. A Geiger–Muller tube.

consisting of a hollow tube or conducting material which acts as one electrode, and a second central wire electrode. In diagnostic work the ionisation chamber is sometimes used for measuring radioactivity for dispensing of isotopes, in this case it is pressurised to obtain reasonable sensitivity. The G.M. tube is used to count gamma rays for large volume *in vitro* tests (e.g. 24-hour urine sample) and also as a beta particle detector for *in vivo* measurements of P-32.

The G.M. Tube
The tube contains a gas, e.g. neon or argon at less than atmospheric pressure (10-50 cm Hg) and a small amount of

quenching vapour, e.g. ethyl alcohol or bromine. The central electrode is thin wire to obtain a high electric field. Tubes are usually operated with a potential difference of 1,200-1,400 volts. The process by which the passage of an ionising particle (electron or beta particle) is detected is as follows:

(i) the beta particle produces ions and secondary electrons,

(ii) the secondary electrons are accelerated in the high electric field and cause further ionisation on their way,

(iii) this cascade of ions moves slowly to the outside wall,

(iv) all the liberated electrons are drawn rapidly to central electrodes to form a single pulse, in less than 1 μs after the event,

(v) the ions reach the outer wall in about 100 μs, during this time the tube is inactive (dead-time), thus restricting the rate at which events can be counted to less than 10^4 per second,

(vi) the quenching vapour prevents a second pulse due to the interaction of the ions with the cathode.

In effect the G.M. tube amplifies the charge produced by the event by a factor of about 10^8. In most cases the pulse across the high resistance (10^5-10^6 ohms) is of the order of 1 volt; sufficiently high to be counted directly by electronic counters.

The main disadvantages of G.M. tubes as gamma ray counters are:

(a) inefficiency (only 1-2% efficient),

(b) inability to discriminate different energies,

(c) large dead-time.

Scintillation Counter

Although it was known for some time that certain crystals produced light flashes when irradiated with rays, it has only been with the advances in electronics that it has been possible to accurately count these flashes and to record the count automatically. A typical scintillation counter is shown in fig. 6-5 with a crystal of sodium iodide for the scintillator. When a gamma ray interacts with the crystal the light produced is detected by a photo cathode in optical contact, which can be achieved by a transparent oil, with the surface of the crystal. The electron pulses produced at the photo cathode are too small to detect without large amplification. The initial amplification is achieved in a photomultiplier tube.

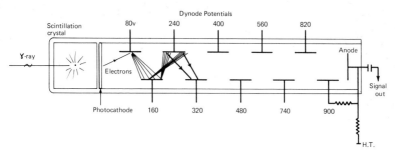

Fig. 6.5. A scintillation detector showing typical dynode potentials.

P.M. Tube
This contains a series of photocathodes (dynodes) with increasing potential difference to accelerate the electrons emitted. At each dynode several electrons are ejected for each electron arriving; thus if there are 10 dynodes and 5 electrons are ejected at each one, the number of electrons arriving at the anode is 5^{10}, or approximately 10^7 electrons. If this current pulse is dropped across a high resistance (10^8-10^9 ohms) the voltage pulse will be 20-200 mV depending on the energy of the gamma ray. This signal can be further amplified 10-1,000 times to give voltages suitable to be counted.

Advantages
    (a) Almost 100% efficiency to gamma rays, if correct counting conditions are chosen for a given situation.
    (b) The output pulse magnitude is proportional to the absorbed energy which allows for a specific gamma-ray energy to be counted by allowing only these pulses through electronic circuits.

Sodium Iodide as a Gamma-Ray Detector
A gamma-ray photon is absorbed in a sodium iodide crystal by one of the three processes, photoelectric, Compton scattering or pair production (see chapter 2). In each case a secondary electron is produced, but the proportion of the energy of the original photon transferred to the electron depends on the specific absorption process. Since it is this electron which produces the scintillation, the amount of light produced

depends on the energy of the electron, and the voltage pulse from the photomultiplier is also dependent on the energy of the electron. If the electron is produced by photoelectric absorption all the energy of the photon is transferred to the electron, except for the portion needed to remove the electron from the K shell of iodine (binding energy 29 keV); the characteristic gamma ray produced is usually immediately absorbed because of its low energy.

In the case of Compton scattering the photon gives only a proportion of its energy to the secondary electron and this is a variable proportion depending on the degree of scatter. The scattered photon may not be absorbed in the crystal. The result is a broad spectrum of pulses corresponding to the total amount of energy gained from the original photon which varies from zero to the Compton edge—the maximum energy transferred to an electron emitted in the forward direction.

Pair production only occurs if the incident photon has an energy greater than 1.02 MeV, thus is only of interest in the case of a few commonly used isotopes (e.g. cobalt-60, sodium-24). An electron and positron are produced with combined kinetic energies equal to the difference between the incident photon energy and 1.02 MeV. At the end of its track the positron absorbs an electron and emits two annihilation quanta each with an energy of 0.511 MeV. If these quanta are totally absorbed a scintillation peak is obtained corresponding to the initial photon energy (n.b. for a positron emitter gamma-rays of 0.511 MeV are always emitted, as well as any other gamma rays, because of the absorption of the positron within the source).

Summary
The overall effects of these different processes may be summarised: (i) for a gamma-ray source emitting low-energy photons <200 keV, the photons will interact mainly by the photoelectric effect and will each produce a similar amount of light, and the voltage pulses will all be of a similar height. A plot of count against voltage produces a curve—the photopeak—of the form shown in fig. 6-6. Unlike the emission spectrum this is not a line because of the random nature of the processes within the crystal. This broadening of the absorption spectrum is energy dependant, the lower the energy the more broadening. The amount of broadening determines the energy resolution of the

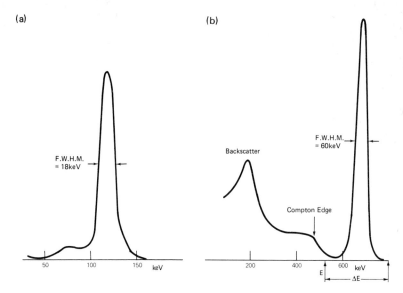

Fig. 6.6. Absorption spectra in sodium iodide showing (a) low energy photons from cobalt 57 producing interactions mainly by the photo-electric effect. (b) High energy photons from caesium 137 showing the photopeak at 660 keV, scatter and the backscatter peak.

crystal, as photon energies which are too close together will not produce separate absorption photopeaks. (ii) For radioisotopes emitting gamma rays of greater than 200 keV there will be a definite fraction absorbed by the photoelectric process that depends on the gamma-ray energy and the size of the absorbing crystal. The photons absorbed by the Compton effect will cause a general spread of the absorption spectrum. (iii) Superimposed on this spectrum, which corresponds to the source alone, may be peaks corresponding to radiation backscattered from surrounding objects, particularly those close to the source where a definite large angle of scatter is needed for the photons to reach the detector. Since the energy of the back scatter is relatively low, e.g. for primary photon energy of 0.3 MeV the backscatter has an energy of 0.14 MeV, it is absorbed mainly by the photoelectric process so producing a photopeak corresponding to the backscattered photon energy. Scatter from walls of the room is reduced by using shielding, often by some means of collimation of the crystal, but also by surrounding the crystal with metal since gamma rays can otherwise pass through the case.

Liquid Scintillation Detector for Beta-Ray Measurements

Sodium iodide crystals are not suitable for most beta-ray sample counting as the outer case of the crystal absorbs beta rays completely even when they are of very high energy.

The most efficient way to measure beta rays is to incorporate the sample in a liquid scintillator. The liquid scintillator can be various substances but always consists of a solvent and a solute. The bulk of the solution is the solvent to dissolve the sample. The actual scintillator may only be 0.5% by weight of the solution. A typical mixture would be:

1 litre of solvent: *p*-dioxane or toluene.
4 g of primary scintillation solute: 2,5-diphenyloxazole (PPO).
0.05 g of secondary scintillation solute: 1,4-bis-2-(-5-phenyl-oxazolyl)-benzene (POPOP).

The detection of the scintillations is made with photocathode-photomultipliers in the usual way. The efficiency of beta-ray counting is still very low, only 2-3% of energy of a beta-ray is converted into light. It is important that the background count level, mainly due to dark current pulses by the photomultiplier tube itself, is reduced as much as possible by cooling the detector.

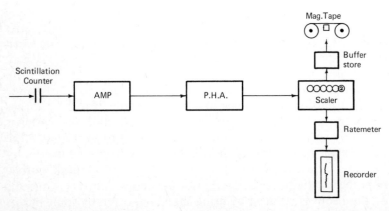

Fig. 6.7. A block diagram of the apparatus associated with a scintillation detector.

ANCILLARY ELECTRONIC EQUIPMENT (fig. 6-7)

Amplifier

To amplify pulses without distortion or attenuation requires a good linear amplifier, this is usually rather bulky and as it is necessarily positioned a few feet away from the detector attenuation of the pulse can occur in the cable. It is sometimes advisable to use a pre-amplifier which can be connected close to the P.M. tube and acts as an impedance matching device between the high output impedance of the P.M. tube and the low cable impedance. This is especially true when low gamma-ray energies are used.

The main amplifier must have the following characteristics:
- (i) good linearity to avoid distortion of pulse amplitude so as to maintain the information about energy distribution,
- (ii) high stability to changes in mains voltage and ambient temperature,
- (iii) able to deal with high frequencies,
- (iv) low noise level.

Pulse Shape

The pulse from the P.M. tube has the shape shown in fig. 6-8, if the rate is high enough these will pile on top of each other, so losing information of an individual pulse height. This shape can be changed by a differentiating circuit (see fig. 12-1d) which produces a sharp output pulse for only fast rising edges at the input.

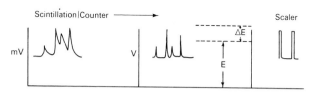

Fig. 6.8. The effect of the various devices on the pulses from the scintillation detector.

Pulse Height Analysis

If it is desired to count only those pulses of a certain voltage amplitude (i.e. certain energy), this can be done electronically in a Pulse Height Analyser. The usual arrangement is to have a variable discriminator bias control that determines the lower level of pulse amplitude accepted; there is a second variable control to set the gate width which determines the voltage range of the pulses that are to be counted. It must be remembered that although a given isotope may only emit one energy, which in theory is a line spectrum, the detector produces a range of pulse voltage due to its inherent resolution. Thus to count all the gamma rays received by the crystal the P.H.A. controls must be set at the levels shown in fig. 6-6. This eliminates the counts due to noise, and Compton scatter.

Scaler
As the pulses come out of the P.H.A. they must be counted and the count displayed in a variety of ways:

   (1) As a total count on a visual display after a specified time interval.
   (2) As a total count punched on paper tape or recorded on magnetic tape after a given time interval.
   (3) As a count rate on a meter or pen recorder.

In both (1) and (2) and sometimes (3) (when a rate is recorded digitally) a counting device known as a scaler is used.

Scale of Two Circuit
At the basis of all scalers is a scale of two-circuit. The principle of the operation of these circuits can be described with reference to the transistor circuit in fig. 6-9. All computing depends on counting in binary on a two-state system. In this case the system is a transistor. If the transistor is conducting (ON) its collector registers a low voltage (state 0), if the transistor is off its collector registers the supply voltage (state 1). In this circuit:

   (i) the collector of transistor A is initially in state 0; and the series resistor ensures that the base of B is below the switching level;
   (ii) the next input pulse raises the base of B so switching the transistor on; this lowers B's collector to a level which switches A off, so that A's collector is in state 1;
   (iii) the next pulse switches A on and thus B off so sending the collector of B to 1.

(a)

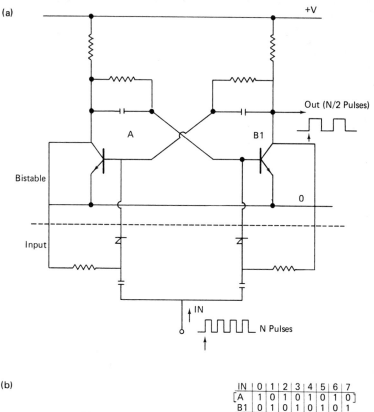

(b)

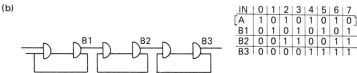

IN	0	1	2	3	4	5	6	7
A	1	0	1	0	1	0	1	0
B1	0	1	0	1	0	1	0	1
B2	0	0	1	1	0	0	1	1
B3	0	0	0	0	1	1	1	1

Fig. 6.9. (a) A basic scale-of-two circuit. (b) A combination of 3 scale-of-two circuits and its associated truth table.

Display

It is possible by arranging a set of n of these two circuits in series to provide a scaling factor of 2^n, and the output of each circuit can be displayed on a light. This is difficult to read quickly, so the binary information is usually converted electronically to decimal and then displayed. The display may be a simple light bulb or it may be a display vacuum tube, e.g. a trochotron tube and Nixie tube. In this system the input pulses from the decimally converted scale of two series cause an electron beam to move sequentially through a series of ten stable positions to illuminate a figure that can be read very easily. Semiconductor devices are also used for display.

Ratemeters
In certain *in vivo* tests the information of radiation intensity is required as a function of time/position in which case the counting rate is needed.

Digital Ratemeter   The most obvious, but less frequently used, way of doing this is to use the scaler to count over a short period of time then display the count, and repeat this sequence continuously. So as not to lose information concerning the rate while transferring it to the display, a buffer may be used to which the count is temporarily transferred to allow the scaler to count while the previous count is processed and displayed.

Analogue Ratemeters   The most common method of measuring count rate is to convert it to a current. This current can be used to drive a simple meter or a pen-recorder or, in the case of scanning, the colour control on the printing system. In the circuit shown (fig. 6-10) each pulse adds a fixed amount of charge to the capacitor, this charge is allowed to leak away through a resistor; a temporary equilibrium is reached when the rate of addition of charge to the capacitor equals the rate of loss of charge through the resistor. The current through the

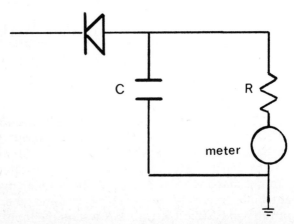

Fig. 6.10. A basic analogue ratemeter circuit.

resistor is measured on a meter. The disadvantages of this measuring system are that it requires calibration and is subject to zero drift.

Time Constant   The size of the resistor and capacitance in the circuit determines the rate at which equilibrium is reached and the time constant $\tau = RC$. If only slow variations in count rate are to be measured this time constant can be large, which has the advantage of smoothing out statistical fluctuations and noise. A fast time constant to follow rapid changes in count rate would be 0.1 sec. But even if a fast time constant is used the recorded rate inevitably lags behind the actual count rate. For most practical purposes this is of no importance; the place where it is most noticeable is in scanning in two directions at relatively high speed, where a scalloping effect is produced that causes a smooth change in dose distribution to be displayed as a zig-zag pattern.

Pen Recorder
The simplest pen recorder uses the same movement as that used in a moving coil meter. To obtain a wider range of movement a potentiometric recorder is used (fig. 6-11) which may have provision for one or more pens. This works on a feed-back servo system which uses the difference in voltage between the input signal and the voltage tapped off by moving a slider on a potentiometric wire to drive the pen along a guide rail. The difference voltage, ΔV, is amplified to drive a servo-motor to

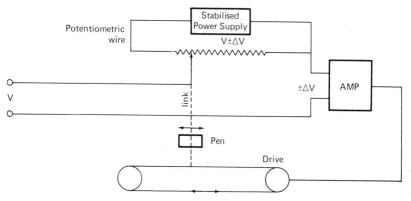

Fig. 6.11. A schematic diagram of a potentiometric recorder.

move the slider to the null position so moving the pen. These recorders usually have a range of chart speeds so that the recording can be made slowly, e.g. cm/min for a renogram, or quickly, e.g. cm/sec for a transit time.

Counting statistics

It would be wrong at this point not to briefly mention the basic limitation on accuracy of counting technique. A radioactive substance emits pulses at random intervals of time; thus in equal intervals of time the same count may not be recorded. Counting of any random events are subject to statistical variations described by the Poisson distribution.

Standard Deviation

If a very large number of measurements of a count within equal time intervals are made (to form the real population distribution) they would have the values shown on the graph (fig. 6-12). If one measurement of the count is now made, the probability that it will fall within the first band of values shown is 68%. The half-width of this band is known as the standard

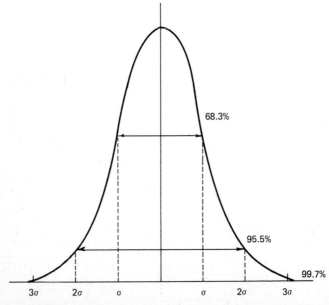

Fig. 6.12. A Poisson distribution of count showing the chance of a single measurement lying within 1σ, 2σ or 3σ of the actual value.

deviation of the count. The standard deviation of a count N is $\sqrt{N}$. The percentage error of any measurement of radioactivity by counting is then $(100 \sqrt{N})/N$ or $100/\sqrt{N}$, i.e. inversely proportional to square root of count; thus to reduce this error as much as possible high count rates are required or counting must be performed over a long period (which requires a very good stability of equipment), e.g. $2,500 \pm 50$, percentage error $= \pm 2\%$; $1,000,000 \pm 1,000\%$, error $= \pm 0.1\%$. n.b. count had to increase by a factor of 400 to decrease error 20-fold.

The limitation on counting for a longer period to obtain an accurate measurement of the activity of the sample only is the level of the background count rate. This background is subject to statistical variations in the same way as the sample count rate and will therefore contribute to the overall inaccuracy of the measurement. Thus if N_c is the total count in time t, and N_b is the background count in the same time, the sample count is given by $N_s = N_c - N_b$. Now the standard deviation of the difference between two measurements is the square root of the sum of the squares of the individual standard deviations; in this case the standard deviation of N_s is $(N_c + N_b)^{1/2}$. The counting rate of the sample is therefore:

$$\frac{N_c - N_b}{t} \pm \frac{(N_c + N_b)^{1/2}}{t^{1/2}}$$

If $N_s = N_b$, the standard deviation is about twice what it would be in the absence of background; if $N_s < N_b$ accurate measurement becomes impossible.

Complete Gamma-Ray Counting Equipment
The basic counting equipment; viz., scintillation counter, H.V. supply, amplifier, P.H.A. scaler, timer, ratemeter, can be obtained in very compact transistorised form. Additional to this is the peripheral equipment that may be needed for holding counters, scanning heads, pen recorders, paper or magnetic tape for computer processing of data, and *in vitro* counting equipment with automatic sample changing.

RADIOISOTOPE TESTS

In vivo Measurements
Measurements of radioactivity within the body can be divided very broadly into two categories: (1) Stationary counting over defined sites of the body, to study the function of an organ—

usually involving the measurement of the change in radio-activity with time; this includes the whole body counter and gamma camera. (2) Moving counter (or patient) to determine the distribution of the radioactivity within the body; this forms part of a scanner or whole-body counter using profile scanning. A gamma-camera is also used to determine distribution of radioactivity. The gamma-camera and whole body counter are discussed separately.

(1) Stationary Counter

This consists of one or more scintillation counters mounted in a stand to allow them to be positioned over organs of the body. Some collimation is required so that radiation from other parts of the body is not received by the counter (see fig. 6-13).

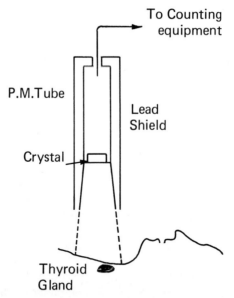

Fig. 6.13. The apparatus for measuring thyroid uptake.

Examples of Use (i) Thyroid Function

One of the first radioactive tests to be performed *in vivo* and now one of the commonest tests performed is the thyroid uptake test. Radioactive iodine (I-131 or I-132) attached to a carrier solution of potassium iodide is given in an oral dose to the patient. The amount of iodine taken up by the thyroid gland is measured by counting at a set distance from the gland a few hours after the dose was given. This count is expressed as a percentage of a given dose counted in the same position in a neck phantom.

In most patients this uptake of iodine measurement is a good indication of the rate of production of thyroid hormone. Different centres have produced their own range of values of uptake to fit different diagnoses found by clinical trial; typical values are:

hyperthyroid patients: 65% after 6 hours;
hyperthyroid patients: 75% after 24 hours;
hypothyroid patients: 15% after 24 hours;
compared with normal (euthyroid): 20-50% after 24 hours.

If radioactive iodine therapy is to be given the uptake is measured daily for 3-5 days to establish the biological half-life of the I-131 to use in the calculation of the dose to be given (see chapter on treatment using radioisotopes).

Details of Thyroid Uptake Test

If a centre deals with large numbers of patients for whom I-131 tests are requested, a stock solution of known activity per unit volume is prepared from which a precise volume can be dispensed. It is only then necessary to count one standard each day, instead of counting every dose given. A dose of about 5 μCi is given orally when the patient has little or no food in the stomach. The activity needs to be low, especially in infants and children, because the radiation dose to the thyroid gland can be 1-3 rads/μCi depending on size of gland and biological half-life of iodide in the patient. Although confined to a relatively small volume this is a high dose of radiation compared to most radiography and indeed most other radioisotope tests. If the patient has the indications of hyperthyroidism a count over the thyroid is performed at 6 hours. If the indications are uncertain a count is made at 24 hours. To obtain sufficient counts for statistical accuracy a counting time of 60-100 seconds must be used. To increase the count rate it is possible to increase the gate width on the pulse-height analyser to include the back-scattered portion of the spectrum, but this introduces the possibility of obtaining different readings of uptake for patients with different neck thicknesses, as the scatter contribution will also be different.

To obtain a measure of the counts received from the surrounding tissue (the blood background) a piece of lead can be held over the thyroid to absorb the radiation, a similar result is obtained by counting over the upper leg. This blood background is then subtracted from the thyroid count and the percentage uptake becomes:

$$\frac{\text{Patient thyroid count} - \text{Blood background}}{S} \times 100\%$$

where S is standard count corrected for background. The standard count is made in a phantom of the dimensions of the average neck with the standard dose placed at about $\frac{1}{2}$ cm from surface, to provide similar absorption and scattering conditions to those in the patient.

(ii) Kidney Function

A pair of matched scintillation counters (i.e. virtually identical crystals and P.M. tubes that would produce identical outputs for the same photon input) positioned over the kidneys are used to detect the accumulation and disappearance of radioactive tracer given intravenously. The recorded traces obtained from the procedure can be interpreted by intercomparison of the two kidney curves or by comparison with normal curves to determine the renal function of the patient.

Details of Technique

The counters are collimated so that no primary radiation from the other kidney is detected (see fig. 6-14). These may be

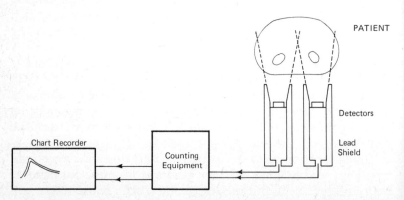

Fig. 6.14. The apparatus for measuring kidney function.

positioned over the back of the patient with the patient sitting or under the patient with the patient lying. The patient should be given at least a pint of water to drink 30 minutes before the test. 20 μCi I-131-labelled hippuran, a substance almost totally extracted from the blood in one passage through the kidneys, is injected intravenously. The count rate from each kidney is recorded in different coloured inks on a pen recorder. A time constant of 10 seconds is suitable for the fast initial phase of the trace, the time constant is then changed to 30 seconds for the rest of the curve. The time of recording is about 15 minutes, during which the patient remains as still as possible.

The Renographic Curve

Patients with normal renal function show a renogram as in fig. 6-15 in which the three phases are shown.

(i) The initial rapid increase in count rate due to the radioactivity appearing in the blood stream in the field of view of the counter.

(ii) The secretion phase corresponding to glomerular filtration and tubular secretion; the count rate rises more slowly than in the initial phase.

(iii) The excretory phase as the secreted hippuran disappears from the field of view of the detector through the upper urinary tract; the count rate falls slowly.

It is the phases (ii) and (iii) that are used in diagnosing malfunction; although the initial spike does provide a useful base line for the measuring of time intervals. A few of the more radical kidney disorders can be illustrated by the renograms in the figures.

(a) Very little secretion—renal artery stenosis.
(b) Excretion completely obstructed.
(c) Complete non-function.

The renogram provides useful information on vascularisation, tubular function, and the passage of urine through the upper urinary tract, with the minimum inconvenience to the patient. As well as aiding the diagnosis of kidney disorders it is a convenient test for follow-up studies after surgery or radio-therapy.

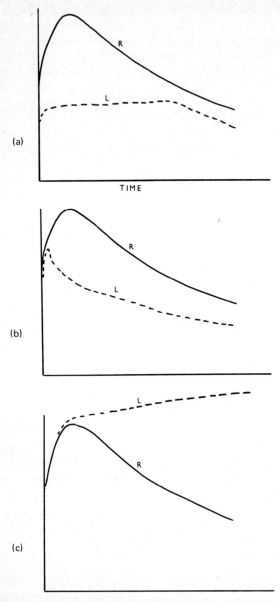

Fig. 6.15. Some examples of the renogram. R—Right kidney (always normal in these examples) L—Left Kidney. (a) Poor secretion in left kidney indicative of renal artery stenosis. (b) Completely non-functioning left kidney. (c) No excretion from left kidney—obstruction of upper urinary tract.

(iii) Cerebral Blood Flow

Another test that uses matched crystals is the study of blood flow through the brain. A counter is placed over each hemisphere of the brain and the count rate from each detector recorded on a pen recorder (fig. 6-16a). The resulting traces can be compared against each other, or against the curve from a normal person.

Details of Test

The counters must be collimated so that the radiation received by each counter is only from one hemisphere of the brain. These are mounted in a special jig positioned over the forehead and angled to avoid the blood pool over the sinuses. A third counter over the heart is useful for recording the appearance of the radioisotope in the main blood stream as a base line for time measurement. The isotope used is technetium-99m in the form of sodium pertechnetate; 1 millicurie in a small volume of solution (0.5 ml) is injected rapidly into a vein in the forearm. The heart counter detects this bolus a few seconds after injection; the counters over the brain respond a few seconds after the heart counter. The count rate reaches a peak then falls quickly to a level corresponding to the isotope remaining in the brain. The actual transit time through the brain is very rapid

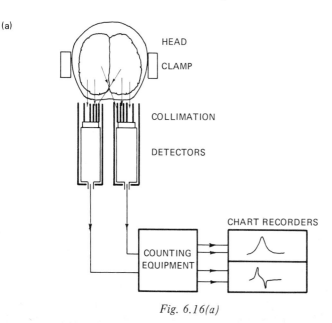

(a)

HEAD
CLAMP
COLLIMATION
DETECTORS
CHART RECORDERS
COUNTING EQUIPMENT

Fig. 6.16(a)

(b)

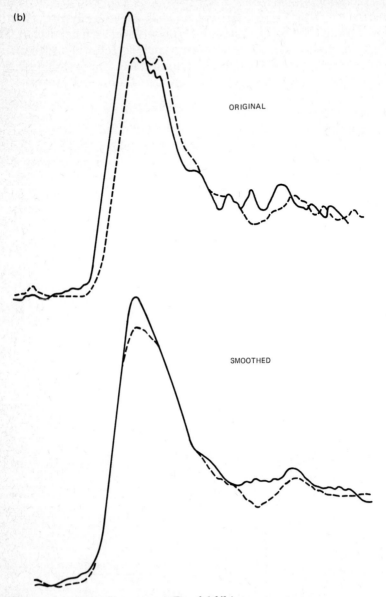

ORIGINAL

SMOOTHED

Fig. 6.16(b)

(c)

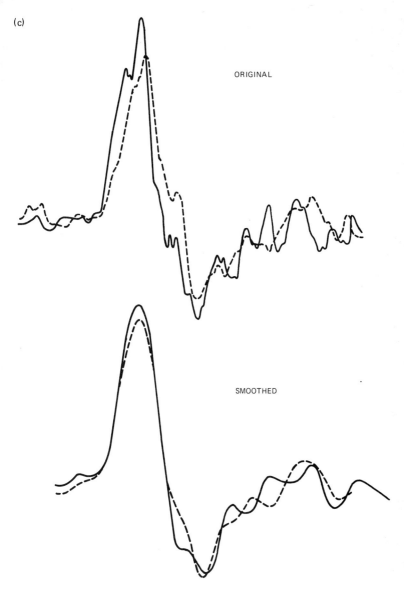

ORIGINAL

SMOOTHED

Fig. 6.16. (a) The apparatus for measuring cerebral transit time. (b) Direct original and smoothed cerebral transit curves. (c) Differentiated original and smoothed transit curves.

(8-12 seconds typically), thus the test is over very quickly and it is vital that all the instrument factors are correct—especially that the ink is flowing in the pens! The traces of count rate for a normal brain are shown in fig. 6-16b, c; the actual transit time is easier to measure on the differentiated trace, especially if any small difference between the traces is to be seen. Computer smoothed curves are also shown.

THE DISTRIBUTION OF RADIOACTIVITY IN THE BODY

Scanning

By moving a scintillation counter in a regular pattern in two dimensions and continuously recording the count rate the distribution of radioactivity over particular parts of the body can be shown as two-dimensional plots of intensity. The usual scanning arrangement is for the patient to lie on a stationary table while the shielded, collimated scintillation counter moves over him (fig. 6-17). The movement is continuous across the patient with a stepped drive longitudinally. The recording of count rate is made, via a ratemeter by either (a) a colour dot recording system moving synchronously with the scan head, (e.g. in a particular nine-colour system the colours are: grey, brown, pale green, blue, violet, orange, red and purple) in which colour and dot rate change with count rate, (b) or as a photodot which is produced by a neon light flashing at a rate proportional to the count rate, recorded on a film which moves synchronously with the scan head. Further features of many modern scanners include:

(i) the lateral speed of scanning can be altered from typically 20-200 cm/min,

(ii) the longitudinal step can be one of four values, e.g. 2, 4, 6 and 12 mm,

(iii) the collimation of the crystal (3- or 5-inch diameter) can be changed depending on the focusing depth, gamma-ray energy of the isotope and sensitivity required,

(iv) scanning can be made uni-directional to avoid the confusing scalloping effects caused by time-lag of the ratemeter behind the real intensity at high speed scanning,

(v) two scanning heads may be fitted, to obtain anterior and posterior scans simultaneously.

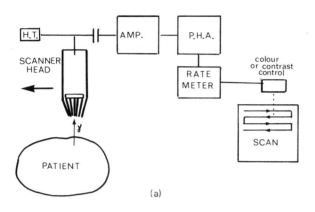

(a)

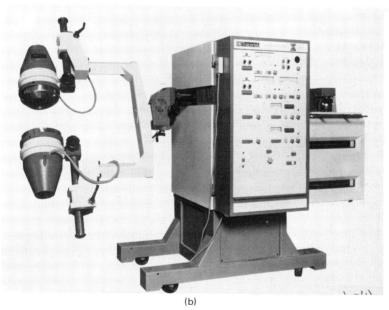

(b)

Fig. 6.17. (a) Schematic diagram of scanner. (b) Photograph of double headed scanner (Courtesy ICN TRACERLAB (U.K.) Ltd.).

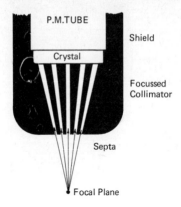

Fig. 6.18. A multichannel collimator.

Collimation

The results produced by any scanning system depend on the sensitivity and resolution of the detection system. To obtain good resolution a narrow collimator is required, but this reduces sensitivity. Multihole collimators increase sensitivity (see fig. 6-18) and can be designed to focus at different distances within the body depending on the organ to be scanned. With low-energy gamma emitters (below 150 keV) these can be made with many holes (100-200 holes for a 5-inch crystal) since the septa between holes can be relatively thin (less than 5 mm lead). This makes technetium-99m (140 keV) a very useful isotope for scanning. If a brain scan is made with technetium-99m using a fine collimator the resolution can be about 1 cm. However, for high-energy gamma rays there is transmission of radiation across the septa of the collimator thus causing loss of resolution. There is an optimum thickness of septa for a given energy at which the increase in resolution must be balanced against loss in sensitivity.

General Scanning Procedure

The patient is injected with the desired compound labelled with an isotope; this is done at a definite time before the scan is to take place, e.g. thyroid scan with technetium-99m—20 minutes; bone scan with ^{99m}Tc-labelled polyphosphate—6 hours.

The detector system conditions are checked to be correct for the isotope used, e.g. P.H.A. settings; the correct collimator is mounted on the scanning head. Then the patient is positioned on the scanner table underneath the head, this is frequently the supine position for the first anterior scan. The scanning head is moved by hand over the site of uptake of the isotope to find the highest count rate. The input to the recording system can then be adjusted so that this count rate corresponds to the maximum recording position, e.g. the colour red on a colour dot system, otherwise the whole range of colour will not be available. The scanning head is then moved to its starting position and set to automatically scan. To avoid wasting time by scanning outside the area of interest the position of the microswitch stops can be continually changed throughout the scan. At the end of the scan a few anatomical points are marked on the scan by positioning the centre of the scanning head (a projected light beam) over each point in turn.

The resulting scan shows an array of differently coloured and differently spaced dots from which, with experience, a consultant can discern various features for diagnostic purposes. However, in some cases a feature (a hot or cold area of radioactivity) is almost obscured by noise, which consists mainly of statistical fluctuations in count rate. In these cases computer analysis, which essentially consists of smoothing out the rapid fluctuations due to noise, is very useful. The scan data is recorded directly on to magnetic tape as actual counts over a definite scan distance, then fed into the computer.

PARTICULAR SCANNING PROCEDURES
Thyroid Scanning

More radioactive iodine is needed to obtain a reasonable scan of the thyroid gland than for the uptake measurement; an oral dose of 25-50 μCi of iodine-131 is given a few hours before the scan is to be made. The anterior scan over the thyroid is the most usual, though the chest is sometimes included when locating metastases from thyroid carcinoma. The scanning speed is about 30 cm/min; the line spacing 0.2 cm. Thyroid scanning in some cases is done with technetium-99m. This can be used to determine thyroid uptake while only giving a fraction of the dose given by iodine-131. Scanning is necessary to determine the background count accurately as this is a higher proportion of the count over the thyroid than with iodine-131. Scanning speed is chosen so that the individual dots can be counted. Counts of dots are made over the thyroid and a background count made by counting dots over an equal area in the background region of the scan.

Diagnostic Uses

Thyroid scanning is usually employed for the following purposes:

(1) the determination of size, shape and position of the thyroid gland, and position of aberrant thyroid tissue,
(2) to allow a comparison of the degree of function of individual areas within the thyroid gland to be made,
(3) determination of quantity of residual thyroid tissue, following surgery or radiotheraphy for treatment of thyroid disease,
(4) detection of distant metastases from thyroid carcinoma.

Brain Scanning

To discover the existence of an abnormality and its position within the brain, the isotope used relies on the breakdown of the blood-brain barrier. The brain tissue is normally impervious to drugs, toxic substances, etc. in the circulating blood, unless there is a disruption by disease or tumour. A very suitable nuclide to use is technetium-99m, in the form of pertechnetate, or indium in the form D.T.P.A. Up to 10 mCi is injected 1-3 hours before the scan is to take place. The patient's head is held in a fixed position with a band across the forehead connected to a head rest. Anterior and lateral scans are taken. It is useful to have an A.P. radiograph of the skull on which the scan can be superimposed, with the head in the scanning position. This can be done with an X-ray set mounted in the ceiling of the scanning room at a distance so as to give little magnification of the skull on the radiograph (fig. 6–19 a & b).

Diagnostic Uses

(1) The location of neoplasms, especially metastatic and pituitary tumours.
(2) To aid diagnoisis of abscesses, aneurysm, and haematoma.

Lung Scanning

The usual lung scan is done using a labelled macroaggregate of human serum albumin injected into the blood stream to display the pulmonary artery blood perfusion. An alternative form of scanning is for the patient to inhale a radioactive gas (Xenon-133) to show the air pathways of the lungs, this will not be discussed here. The particle size of the albumin is important if the best scan is to be obtained. The particles must occlude a small proportion of vascular pathways in the lung for a time to allow the scan to be made, but must not block too many pathways for too long. The isotopes used to label the macro-aggregates are iodine-131 (200 μCi) or technetium-99m (1 mCi). It is usual only to make an anterior scan; it is useful to have a chest radiograph of the patient in the scanning position on which to superimpose the scan.

Diagnostic Uses

It is important to realise that the lung scan detects only blood flow through the lungs and not lung morphology or function. Thus a very important clinical use is the early diagnosis of pulmonary embolism, as it may show the obstruction at a time when medical or surgical treatment has a greater chance of success. It is also useful in visualising the extent of pulmonary emphysema and also the extent of disruption of blood flow caused by a lung tumour.

Liver Scanning

The most suitable substances for liver uptake studies are colloids, e.g. antimony sulphide labelled with technetium-99m. One millicurie of this tracer is given intravenously before the scan is to be made. An anterior and lateral scan are usually performed.

Diagnostic uses

The liver does not show up well on the normal radiograph because of its soft tissue composition. The liver scan is of great use in displaying the size, outline and position of organ in the body. Liver scans are also used to localise within the liver space occupying lesions, primary and secondary tumours, cysts and abscesses.

IN VITRO RADIOISOTOPE TESTS

Radioisotope tests involving either (i) the giving of a labelled substance, usually in the form of an intravenous injection, and then determining the activity of samples of body fluids, or (ii) the use of radioactive materials in quantitative analysis of body fluids instead of chemical analysis, are routine in hospitals now and will be used more and more in the future. Most of the work

(a)

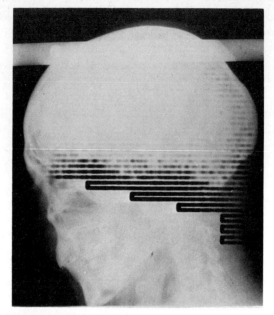

Lat.

(b)

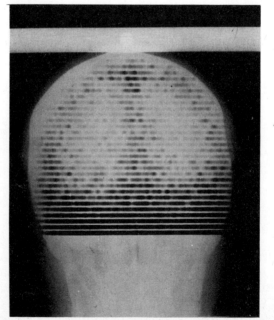

A.P.

(a)

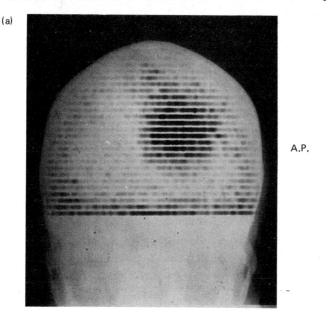

A.P.

(b)

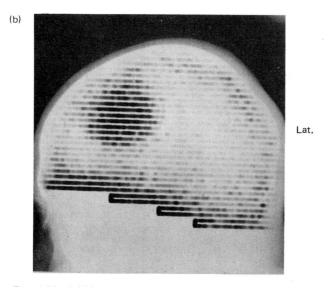

Lat.

Fig. 6.19. (a) Normal Brain Scan. Lat., A.P. (b) Abnormal
Brain Scan. A.P., Lat.

involves gamma emitters in small volumes of fluid for which a well-type scintillation counter is ideal; in the case of gamma emitters in large volumes, e.g. 24-hour urine samples, a large counter, e.g. a ring of G.M.-tubes can be useful; for work with beta emitters—mainly carbon-14 and tritium—a liquid scintillation counter is necessary.

Well-Scintillation Counter

The samples to be counted are in small bottles. To detect radiation efficiently from these, i.e. so there is little self-absorption in the sample, the crystal of the counter contains a cylindrical hole (fig. 6-20). A crystal that will meet most needs

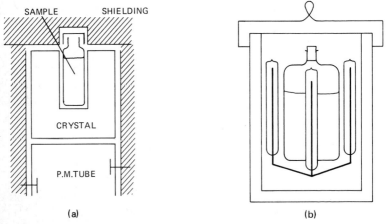

Fig. 6.20. (a) A well-scintillation detector. (b) A ring of G.M. tubes for large volume γ-emitters.

is a Na(Tl)I 3-inch diameter, 3-inch length that will contain a hole 1-inch diameter, 2-inch length, so that there is 1-inch thickness of crystal surrounding a sample. This thickness is necessary for counting the higher energy gamma emitters (e.g. cobalt-58) efficiently. This crystal is mounted in a "well" of lead to reduce the background radiation to a low level. This is because many of the samples will only contain a fraction of one microcurie, so the count rate will be low and an increase in the difference between this count rate and the background count rate is vital in the accuracy of the technique. This well-scintillation counter may be a simple "lead castle"

Fig. 6.21. Single sample well crystal and complete measuring equipment (Courtesy J & P Engineering).

standing by itself and connected to the counting equipment (fig. 6-21), or it may be part of an automatic sample changer.

Automatic sample changer

In a busy isotope department there will be many samples counted each day and each sample will need about 15 minutes counting time to obtain sufficient counts for statistical purposes. Thus an automatic system of feeding in the bottles is essential. There are a number of commercial sample changers available (e.g. see fig. 6-22) based on a continuous-feed system of up to three hundred samples. The bottles can be placed anywhere on the hoop and the apparatus programmed to start at the first bottle, work through to the last required bottle and then start again at the first. The system is fully automatic so that the count, time of count and position of sample are typed out on a teletypewriter or punched on paper tape. This allows samples to be put on last thing at night and the results obtained the following morning. If the results are obtained on paper tape this can be fed into a computer which is programmed to calculate the result of the test directly.

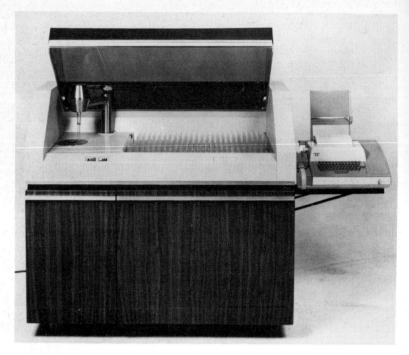

Fig. 6.22. 500 sample, cassette loading gamma counter (Courtesy ICN TRACERLAB (U.K.) Ltd.

Setting the Controls of a Sample Changer

The actual counting equipment in a sample changer is the same as for any basic scintillation counting equipment. The pulses are amplified and analysed before being counted on a scaler. For certain tests it is advantageous to have two separate counting channels (e.g. Vitamin $B_{1\,2}$ absorption using Co-57 and Co-58). Stability of the H.T. unit supplying the P.M. tube and of the amplifier are essential in apparatus in continuous use. To check for electronic drift the spectrum of iodine-131 is plotted periodically.

To make it possible to count an isotope its spectrum must be plotted and a suitable range of energy over which to integrate is chosen, and the P.H.A. and amplifier settings recorded on a chart on the sample changer. It is *not* usual to alter the H.T. for different isotopes.

The sample activity is usually unknown, so as well as setting a counting time it is desirable to set a number of counts, e.g.

20,000, otherwise too few counts may be recorded. When this count is reached the sample changer stops counting the sample and removes it from the well crystal while the counting time is typed out.

Some Common in vitro Tests using Gamma Emitting Radioisotopes

In vitro tests can be divided generally into the following groups:

(1) Dilution tests: e.g. red cell volume, plasma volume, total exchangeable potassium and sodium.
(2) Absorption tests: e.g. absorption of vitamin B_{12}, absorption of iron, absorption of calcium.
(3) Metabolism turnover studies: e.g. red cell life.
(4) Leakage tests: e.g. blood leaking into G.I. tract.
(5) Analytical tests, particularly saturation analysis.

Models Used in Tracer Studies

To understand the results obtained from tracer studies, models of the body must be used to which mathematical equations can be fitted. The models are described in terms of compartments, which may be anatomical, physiological, chemical or physical subdivisions within the body of the substance concerned, e.g. there are broadly two compartments for sodium or potassium within the intracellular and extra-cellular spaces. The amount of tracee[1] within any compartment is known as the pool. To determine the amount of tracee in a compartment and the rate of movement from one compartment to the next by any of the models described below requires the following assumptions to be made: (a) that within each compartment the tracer is rapidly mixed with the tracee as soon as it enters the pool, so that there is full mixing before any tracee leaves the pool; (b) that the system is in a steady state.

Closed Single Compartment (Dilution Analysis)

This is based on the very simple principle that if a known small volume of fluid containing a labelled substance is thoroughly mixed with an unknown large volume of fluid the large volume can be determined from the amount of labelled substance in a sample taken from it. In terms of radioisotope tests this

[1] The tracee is the substance whose path through the body is to be studied by means of the tracer.

"density" is determined from the number of counts detected from a small sample of the volume to be determined, which can be compared with the number of counts from the given dose. Thus, if the measured activity in the volume, V, given to the patient is A/unit volume and the activity in a sample, volume v, from the patient is a/unit volume, then the volume of the pool of liquid into which the isotope was injected is Av/a. This simple proportion principle relies on there being no loss of labelled compound.

Red Cell Mass (see fig. 6-23)
A blood sample of 10 ml is removed from the patient and immediately put in a bottle containing A.C.D. The plasma is removed by centrifuging, at only about 1,500 r.p.m. to avoid damaging the red cells, and the supernatant extracted. This is mixed with sterile saline to be used to wash the red cells. The red cells are labelled with 30 μCi of chromium-51 in the form of sodium chromate. They are left with the added dose for 40 minutes during which time they should be kept at about body temperature. The unattached radioactive chromium is then

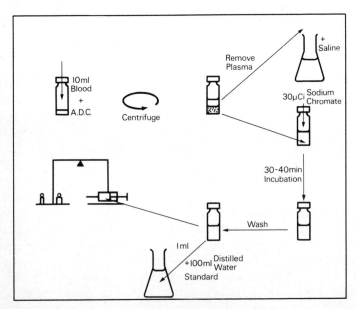

Fig. 6.23. The steps in preparing labelled red cells for determining red cell volume by dilution analysis.

removed by washing the cells several times with plasma saline mixture. The red cells are then drawn into a syringe and made up to about 10-15 ml with plasma/saline which is weighed before and after injection to obtain the mass of red cells injected. A blood sample is taken after about 20 minutes; the red cells spun down in a centrifuge, weighed, then counted. This sample may be one of three or four taken to determine red cell life, as described below.

Diagnostic Uses
This is the only accurate absolute red cell volume method—especially useful before treatment for polycythemia and during follow up after treatment.

Other Dilution Tests

	Nuclide
Plasma Volume	^{99m}Tc
	^{125}I–H.S.A.
	^{131}I–H.S.A.
Exchangeable sodium	^{24}Na
Total exchangeable potassium	^{42}K

OTHER MODELS

Open Single Compartment
A compartment in which there is continuous loss of tracee by excretion, etc. can be described by a model consisting of a tank of water with a hole in it. The rate of change of the volume within the tank depends directly on the volume within the tank: $dV/dt = -kV$; where k is the rate constant. This is yet another example of the rate of change of a quantity depending on the instantaneous value of the quantity, and may thus be described by the exponential equation: $V = V_0 e^{-kt}$. Thus if definite amount of tracer is introduced suddenly into the compartment the tracer concentration within the pool falls as $dA/dt = -kA$. Thus if samples are taken from the pool at subsequent time intervals the rate constant k may be determined. This procedure is used to determine plasma iron clearance (fig. 6-24). Extrapolation of the points back to zero time will give a value of the tracer concentration corrected for any loss which may have occurred; this can be used to determine plasma volume.

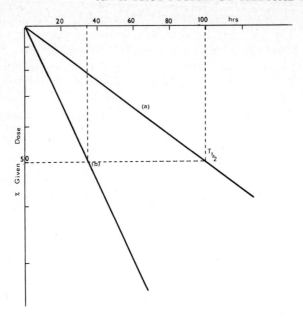

Fig. 6.24. Plasma iron clearance curves for a typcial (a) normal and (b) a patient suffering from polycythemia.

The situation in a compartment in which there is a steady inflow of tracer as well as an outflow is more complicated. The resultant rate of change of tracer is given by: $(dA/dt) = P - kA$; where P is the inflow. The integral of this is $A = P/k (1 - e^{-kt})$; i.e. the activity builds up to a steady-state level of $A = P/k$.

Open Two Compartment System
Consider the system in fig. 6-25 in which one compartment is in series with a second. In a steady state, the flow into and out of compartment 1 is the same as the flow into and out of compartment 2. If an initial quantity of tracer is suddenly put into 1 the flow out of 1 will be as above, i.e. $A_1 = 100 e^{-k_1 t}$; if the quantity of isotope is 100 units. The rate of change of activity in 2 is given by:

$$\frac{dA_2}{dt} = k_1 A_1 - k_2 A_2, \quad \text{or} \quad \frac{dA_2}{dt} = k_1 \cdot 100 e^{-k_1 t} - k_2 A_2.$$

If this is integrated the activity in compartment 2 is given by:

$$A_2 = \frac{100 k_1}{k_2 - k_1} (e^{-k_1 t} - e^{-k_2 t}).$$

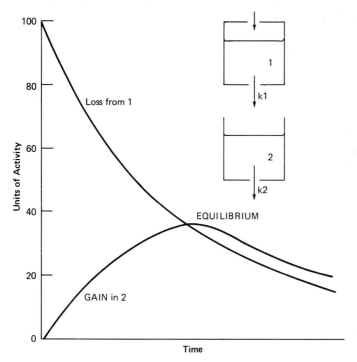

Fig. 6.25. A schematic diagram to illustrate an open two compartment system.

As well as being useful in a precursor-product relationship in the body this also describes the parent/daughter relation in radio-active decay.

Absorption Tests

With the aid of radioisotope techniques it is possible to track the amount of a given tracer into the different compartments of the body, which forms a valuable research tool and, in some cases, e.g. vitamin B_{12}, a valuable diagnostic tool.

Absorption of Vitamin B_{12}

The absorption of vitamin B_{12} in the small intestine can be assessed either indirectly by finding how much is excreted in faeces or urine, or directly by using a whole-body counter. The biological half-life of vitamin B_{12} is about one year so it is important to use an isotope that will deliver a relatively low dose; ^{57}Co or ^{58}Co are suitable isotopes for this test. The measurement of B_{12} absorption is a two-stage procedure to differentiate diagnosis. The test is first carried out by giving the patient a small oral dose of radioactive B_{12} alone. If the patient does not absorb the B_{12} normally the test is then repeated with the addition of Intrinsic Factor (I.F.).

Urinary Excretion Method
The patient has fasted overnight and empties his bladder before the test. A dose of 1 μCi of cobalt-58- or cobalt-57-labelled B_{12} is given by mouth, following an intramuscular injection of 1 mg of non-radioactive B_{12}. All urine is collected for 24 hours. This can be counted as a whole sample in a ring of G.M. tubes (fig. 6-20b), or a spot sample may be taken and counted in a well-scintillation counter. The result is expressed as a percentage of the given dose. The test is repeated with a dose of labelled B_{12} and intrinsic factor.

Brief Analysis of Results
Normal subjects excrete 10% or more of a dose of 1 μg B_{12} in 24 hours. Patients with pernicious anaemia excrete less than 5%; this is improved to 10-15% when I.F. is added. In diseases of the intestinal mucosa the absorption may be low even when intrinsic factor is added.

There is now a kit available with B_{12} labelled with cobalt-58 and B_{12} with I.F. labelled with cobalt-57. As the energies of these are far apart, they can be counted simultaneously using two pulse-height analysers and scalers.

Other Absorption Tests

	Nuclides used	Detection System
Calcium	^{45}Ca, ^{47}Ca, ^{85}Sr also ^{99m}Tc	Well-scintillation counter or whole-body counter
Iron	^{59}Fe	Well-scintillation counter or whole-body counter.

Metabolism Turnover Studies
The most important test in this category is that of red-cell life. The basis of this test has already been described.

Interpretation of Red-Cell Survival Results

The radioactive label on red cells is not permanent and may be removed before the death of the cell, thus it is impossible to obtain a precise mean cell life. However, the information is valuable if it can be compared with normal patients obtained under the same conditions. The test is useful in the following instances:

(i) in diseases where the life-span of cells is shortened by an intracorpuscular defect, e.g. hereditary anaemia;

(ii) where the life-span is shortened by an external factor such as a faulty replacement heart valve.

Leakage Tests

Radioisotopes are useful in many fields of science involving the detection of fluid (including gaseous) leaks from a system, as very small quantities can be difficult to detect. This is true of the human body in which it can be difficult to detect a small internal haemorrhage.

Detection of Gastro-Intestinal Haemorrhage

If the red cells are labelled with ^{51}Cr a haemorrhage of as small as 5 ml may be detected in the faeces. This is to be compared with normal individuals where there is a daily blood loss of about 1 ml.

Saturation Analysis

A number of analytical techniques using radio-isotopes have come into use since 1960; although they have been given different names, e.g. radioimmunoassay, they can be grouped together as methods of analysis which are based on the partition of a substance into two parts: (a) that which has not reacted with a given reagent, i.e. remaining in the free state; (b) that which has become bound to the reagent. If the amount of reagent remains constant, the ratio of the amount of the substance in the free state to the amount in the bound state depends on the original concentration. Thus a graph can be drawn of the form shown in fig. 6-26 from which the concentration of the compound can be determined. The technique uses the principle of dilution analysis to determine the amount of reagent in each fraction. Since the technique is based on radioactive measurement, where effectively each molecule of

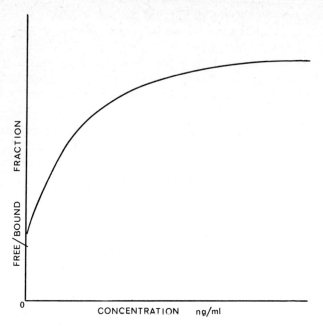

Fig. 6.26. The form of a typical saturation analysis curve.

the labelled reagent can be counted, the analysis is very sensitive, with a lower limit of the order of pico-grams per millilitre; thus the method can be used to measure hormones and other physiologically important substances at concentrations in which they are found in the blood, e.g. thyroxine, vitamin B_{12}, insulin.

Practical Points
The substance to be measured must be available labelled with a suitable isotope, e.g. vitamin B_{12} labelled with cobalt-57. The isotope has two functions to perform: (1) it monitors the extraction of the substance to be measured from the blood sample, (2) it is used to measure the distribution into free and bound compartments. It may be advisable to use two different isotopes to perform these functions. The labelled substance P is added to the sample containing P from the patient; after a suitable time interval P is extracted from the sample, if this is necessary to avoid competing reactions. The binding agent Q, which reacts specifically with P, is then added. After incubation

Q has become bound to a proportion of P. The free and bound fractions of P can then be separated by various techniques, of which the most common is the adsorption of the free fraction to charcoal or an ion-exchange resin. The amount of P in each fraction is determined from the amount of radioactive P by counting in a sample counter. The ratio is used to determine the quantity of P from standard curves.

RADIOISOTOPE CAMERAS

Scanning methods for obtaining a picture of the distribution of radioactivity within the body suffer from several disadvantages.

    (i) the information is displayed on a series of lines,
   (ii) there are discrete levels of count rate,
  (iii) scanning is usually performed only in horizontal plane.

It is highly desirable to have a method of obtaining the distribution of radioactivity in the body as a single picture. If such a picture could be obtained in a short exposure time, the change in distribution with time could be observed.

    Gamma rays travel in straight lines in the same way as light, but unfortunately they cannot be refracted to form an image through a lens. However, the simplest light camera is the pin-hole camera in which the image is formed simply by light from the object passing through a pin-hole so that one spot on the object forms only one spot of the image as in fig. 6·27. If a pin-hole is made in thick lead so that gamma rays can only pass through the hole a simple gamma-ray camera is formed that can image gamma-ray sources. The image can be produced on film in the same way as a light camera, but unless the radiation

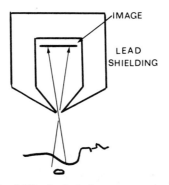

Fig. 6.27. A pin-hole gamma camera.

intensity is very high the exposure time to produce a good image on the film is too long to be of clinical use. Even if a fluorescent screen is used in front of the film that effectively amplifies the gamma radiation by converting it to light, the exposure time to produce an image of a source, e.g. thyroid gland containing several millicuries of a radioisotope, is at least one hour. There is a method of seeing the image cast on the fluorescent screen or scintillation crystal without using film. An array of photomultiplier tubes is used, each one looking at a definite section of the scintillation crystal. The position of each P.M. tube is related to a position on an oscilloscope screen. Thus if a scintillation occurs in front of one P.M. tube it will be

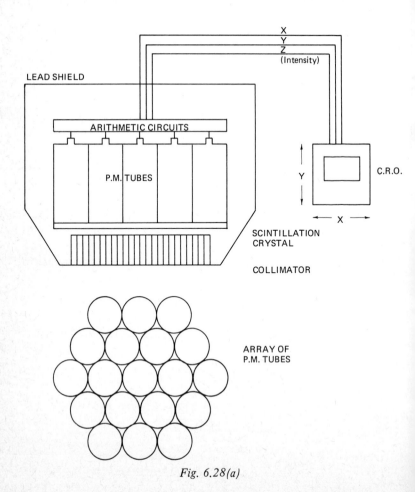

Fig. 6.28(a)

displayed at that position on the C.R.O.; if a scintillation occurs between P.M. tubes, almost half the light reaches each tube and the position can be determined. If a large number of P.M. tubes are used, as is necessary to obtain useful resolution, a small computing circuit is necessary to sort out the proportions of signals from a given scintillation to fix its position on the display screen. The total magnitude of the signal is also found so that pulse-height analysis may be used in the same way as with a single crystal/P.M. tube.

A number of commercial gamma cameras are now available and operate on the above principles, they all have the following features:

(1) A single large sodium iodide crystal of 11 inches diameter, $\frac{1}{2}$-inch thick, this limits the photon energy range to 140-400 keV.

(2) An array of 19 P.M. tubes (this strange number can be seen to arise from the symmetrical arrangement within the circle of the crystal, see fig. 6-28. These must be well-matched tubes with well-stabilised H.T. supply to obtain accurate pictures.

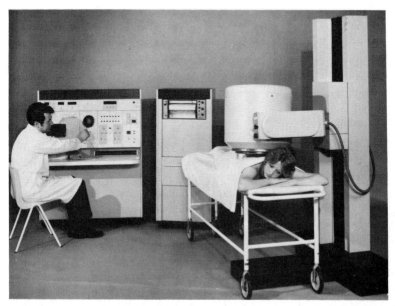

Fig. 6.28. (a) A schematic diagram of a multichannel collimator gamma camera. (b) Photograph (Courtesy Nuclear Enterprises Ltd.).

(3) Heavy lead surround to reduce background radiation—this is essential with such a large crystal.

(4) Electrically driven movements to position the head (weighing several hundredweight) at any angle over the patient.

(5) Choice of collimator.

A choice of collimator is desirable for the following reason. Although the basic pin-hole is an attractive means of directly imaging, only a very small amount of radiation is detected and the system is very insensitive. To use much more of the radiation without losing geometrical resolution a multiple-hole collimator usually with parallel holes can be used. Each hole allows radiation from only a small area of the radioactive source to reach the scintillator—thus the information about the object received at the crystal is very similar to the image from a pin-hole camera.

Uses of Gamma Camera

The gain in sensitivity over scanning because of crystal size is about ten times with a parallel-hole collimator which allows an exposure time of 0.5-2 minutes to be used. This means that if sequential images are produced the change in distribution of radioactivity with time can be obtained. This is especially useful in the study of kidney function.

WHOLE-BODY COUNTERS

Very sensitive detection systems are necessary for counting very small quantities of radioactive materials within the body. Basically this is achieved by surrounding the body with large scintillation detectors, however this leads to the problem of a background level of counts from cosmic radiation, radiations emitted from the earth and building materials. Thus either the complete room holding the whole-body counter must be very well shielded or the counters themselves must be well shielded.

For measuring natural radiation within the body the former arrangement is necessary with walls of lead 4 inches thick; this is very expensive and for clinical work, where the activity levels are of the orders of 1 μCi, less stringent requirements are necessary. A satisfactory system utilises a shadow shield which shields background radiation reaching the crystals to a satis-factory level (fig. 6-29). One commercial system uses two

Fig. 6.29. Whole Body Shadow Shield Monitor (Courtesy Nuclear Enterprises Ltd.).

scintillation crystals 8 x 4 inches above and below the patient who is moved between the crystals on a motor-driven couch. The collimation of the detectors can be adjusted from full-field for whole-body counting to a slit for profile scanning.

Uses of Whole-Body Counters
Absorption of iron (using ^{59}Fe) or vitamin B_{12} (using ^{58}Co) can be studied directly by measuring activity in the patient immediately after the dose has been given, then following the level of activity remaining in the body from day to day. This gives a much more direct estimate of absorption than excretion methods.

Profile Scanning
This can be used to assess the general longitudinal distribution of radioactivity, for example, thyroid carcinoma secondaries can be detected with a tracer dose of I-131.

CHAPTER 7

Protection from Ionising Radiation

THE HAZARD OF IONISING RADIATION

Following the rapid implementation of X-rays for diagnostic purposes at the beginning of the twentieth century the dangers of exposure to the radiologist to these rays did not immediately become apparent. However, after only a few years, especially in cases where the radiologist had frequently kept his hands in the radiation beams for some time, it became evident that these rays could have a devastating effect. These early radiologists suffered from skin erythema sometimes leading to ulceration and eventually, in some cases, to radiation-induced cancer. The ironic fact is that this very effect is used to cure cancer, if the radiation is given in a controlled manner. This was the first evidence to man of the damaging effects of ionising radiations. Since that time precautions have been taken in every field, both medical and industrial, where ionising radiations are used; the dose to personnel has been reduced to such a level that these have very little effect. However, evidence of the damage which can be produced in man, especially the long-term damage, has come in from other sources; radiation accidents by ingestion of radioisotopes, whole-body irradiation from a nuclear reactor, and two atomic bomb explosions over the heavily populated cities of Hiroshima and Nagasaki. The information of the radiation effects on man gleaned from these events has aided the establishment of codes of practice on the acceptable levels of exposure, both for external radiations and internal radiation from injected radioisotopes.

RADIATION EFFECTS

Whatever the type of radiation incident on a biological entity, it is the ionisation produced—the number of ions and their density—which determines the effect of the radiation on the system. The effects are still not fully understood, but there appear broadly to be two types of effect:

(i) direct effects in which a vital molecule of a cell is damaged irreparably; but this does not account for the total effect.

(ii) indirect effects caused by changes in composition of the medium surrounding a vital structure, e.g. the decomposition of water into the highly active radicals O^+ and OH^- which can in turn affect a key molecule in a structure.

Mathematical models can be applied to experimental data from cell cultures which have been irradiated and produce cell survival curves which describe the number of cells remaining after a given dose of radiation. These are basically exponential in nature, usually with a slight shoulder in the initial part of the curve due to some sort of threshold effect.

Radiotherapy is a successful method of killing tumour cells while sparing the surrounding tissue because tumour cells are more radiosensitive than normal cells. This appears to be in part due to the fact that tumour cells are more active than normal cells. Similarly certain parts of the body are more sensitive to radiation than others, and will be the first to suffer in a radiation accident.

Acute Whole-Body Radiation
Thus when doses of radiation are given to the whole body it is mainly the haemotopoietic and gastrointestinal systems which suffer first, within 24 hours following irradiation. A dose to a level exceeding 50 rads produces nausea, vomiting and diarrhoea, known as acute radiation syndrome. At dose levels of 400-500 rads symptoms persist and 50% of a population receiving this dose die within 2-3 months, mainly from the effects of diarrhoea and internal haemorrhage.

Late Effects
At lower levels of radiation dose there may be little or no immediate effect. The effects of a few rads may not be seen for tens of years, or even the next generation, or not at all. It is these long-term effects that have determined the permissible levels of exposure to personnel and to the population in general.

Radiation-Induced Cancer

The risks of induction of disorders such as leukaemia are so small that they must be expressed in the following rather complicated statistical jargon. The normal incidence of leukaemia depends on the part of the world, but varies in the range 20-70 new cases per year per million of population. The studies on Hiroshima and Nagasaki victims show a significant increase in the number of cases of leukaemia in Japan. The evidence from persons receiving 100 rads or more shows that the incidence of new cases appearing each year in the fifteen years subsequent to exposure was 100 new cases per million per 100 rads. This can be extrapolated, although this procedure is not necessarily valid, to give a figure for any given population or dose level of about one extra case per year per million man-rads. The risk of induction of thyroid carcinoma and risk of induction of other types of carcinoma both give similar figures.

Genetic Effects

These are of two types:

    (i) if the foetus is irradiated *in utero* there appears to be a slight increase in the risk of induction of leukaemia for the infant.

    (ii) irradiation of the gonads introduces a small risk of producing congenital handicaps in offspring at some later date.

Acceptable Dose Levels

The hazards of ionising radiations sound alarming, but must be seen in the perspective of other risks that are taken in everyday life; the risk of an accident causing death or serious injury to an individual when travelling by car is of the order of one in a thousand of the population each year.

Any dose level set as a maximum to be received by personnel working in a particular field must take into consideration the facts:

    (i) that the job must be done,

    (ii) it must be done as well as possible without unnecessary risk,

    (iii) that an individual inescapably receives background radiation.

Background Radiation

A typical figure for the level of background radiation is 100 millirads per year, but as a large part of this is terrestrial in origin it can vary from place to place over the earth.

Maximum Permissible Levels of Radiation Dose for Personnel Working in Medical and Dental Fields

Details of the handling of radiation sources and radioactive materials are given in the national and local codes of practice set by the International Committee on Radiation Protection. To summarise the present maximum permissible dose levels set by the International Committee on Radiation Protection:

(a) for the situation where the whole body may be irradiated with X-rays or gamma rays the maximum permissible dose is 3 rads in any one period of 13 weeks; in addition it is recommended that the cumulative dose should not be permitted to exceed 5 rads per year of age above 18 years. i.e. $D = 5(N - 18)$ rads;

(b) the situation of the whole body being irradiated uniformly is rare, so levels for parts of the body are set as follows:

skin, thyroid and bone	30 rads in a year
hands, forearms, feet and ankles	75 rads in a year
all other single organs	15 rads in a year
(particularly important as regards ingestion)	

HAZARD ASSESSMENT AND RADIATION PROTECTION

When a new piece of equipment is to be installed that emits or utilises X- or gamma radiation, there are various steps that are taken to ensure the radiation safety of patients and staff. If a new building is to accommodate the equipment, it can be built to a specification of design and materials to limit radiation escaping to inhabited areas. There are national rules concerning the levels of radiation desirable in terms of leakage from machines, but shielding of the machine depends on the local conditions, e.g. setting of windows or occupancy of rooms, and barriers must be chosen so that any personnel working in the vicinity are kept well within the maximum permissible dose. To ensure that this is the case, especially where equipment has been installed in accommodation which has had to be altered to take it, an area survey must be made. Finally, and this is most important as it is the ultimate check on all parameters, the staff are constantly monitored with personnel monitors (film badge) to discover any fault in the protection measures—either in the chosen barriers, or rules of operation.

Room Design

In reducing any radiation hazard the same principles apply to all radiation sources:

(1) barriers must be erected of sufficient absorbing power to reduce the dose rate beyond them to an acceptable level for personnel within the vicinity. Many factors need to be considered when deciding on the thickness of barrier, but of vital importance is whether or not the primary radiation is incident on the barrier; generally the primary dose rate differs from the secondary (scatter and leakage) radiation dose rate by a factor of about 1,000.

(2) to ensure that the distance between source and personnel is as large as is conveniently possible as this makes use of the very valuable reduction in dose rate due to inverse square law.

Diagnostic X-Ray (see fig. 7-1)

Most building materials provide adequate protection from scattered radiation from diagnostic X-rays. For example: at 70 kVp a normal clay brick, $4\frac{1}{2}$ inches thick, will attenuate the intensity of primary radiation by a factor of 1/10,000, the equivalent attenuation resulting from 1 mm lead. In this energy range lead equivalence is often referred to for convenience when different materials are used. Where the primary beam is incident on a barrier which shields personnel the thickness should be increased to 2 mm lead equivalence; this corresponds to 2 bricks or 1 brick plus $\frac{3}{8}$-inch barium plaster, or 6-inch concrete. The control console has a viewing window of lead glass.

In diagnostic X-ray rooms the exposures are usually short, during which time staff stand behind the control console; during screening operations where staff necessarily need to be near the patient lead-rubber aprons are worn to protect the whole of the trunk from scattered radiation.

There are usually no door interlocks in diagnostic rooms, but it is recommended that a warning light is placed over the door that is automatically lit when an exposure is about to be made.

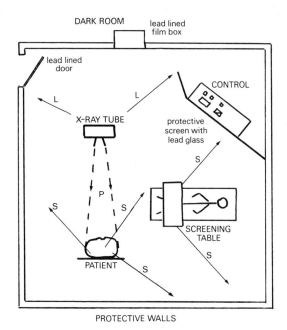

Fig. 7.1. An X-ray diagnostic room showing various aspects of protection. P—primary, S—scattered, L—leakage radiation.

THERAPY ROOMS

The time of radiation exposure is much longer in therapy than diagnosis, and at high energies the dose rates are much higher and the radiation more penetrating; thus barriers, interlocks and rules are more comprehensive than in diagnostic use.

Low Energy

The barrier thicknesses for superficial therapy treatment rooms are similar to those for diagnostic X-ray rooms. The only feature to stress is that no member of staff must be in the room during treatment, as the leakage and scatter of radiation would very soon exceed the maximum permissible dose level. After the patient has been positioned correctly all staff must leave the room and the machine is operated from outside. There should be a door interlock to prevent the switching on of X-rays unless the door is shut. This is especially vital with these machines as they can be directed so that the beam is pointing at the door. The door itself should contain lead sheet at least $1\frac{1}{2}$ mm thick.

Medium Energy

The wall thickness needs to be increased to a lead equivalence of 10 mm (e.g. about 16-inch concrete) to absorb the primary beam. The secondary radiation barrier should have a lead equivalence of 5-6 mm. This includes the door, which must be sited so that it is never in line with the primary beam.

High Energy

With higher energy radiations their great penetrating power is a problem, especially since atomic number is no longer important in limiting penetration as photoelectric absorption is far outweighed by Compton scattering effects; thus all materials of similar thickness (in g/cm^2) absorb high-energy radiation equally.

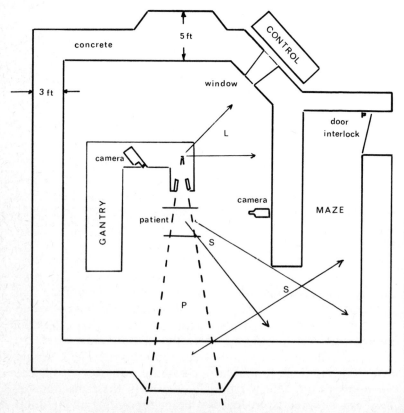

Fig. 7.2. A High Energy Radiotherapy room.

To reduce the dose levels sufficiently, without excessive cost, the only suitable material is concrete. The primary barrier for 4 MV X-rays needs to be 5-6 feet of concrete, this thickness can be reduced proportionally by using the denser form of concrete, barytes concrete, which has a density of about 3.2 g/cm^3 instead of the normal 2.2 g/cm^3. The secondary radiation barrier needs to be $2\frac{1}{2}$-3 feet of concrete.

These enormous thicknesses introduce the problem of room access and viewing. Any form of door which also acts as a radiation barrier is out of the question in a busy department, thus a specially shaped entrance hall (a maze) must be built (see fig. 7-2). This acts as a multiple reflector of the incident radiation so that by the time it reaches the end of the maze nearly all the energy has been dissipated. Windows can be made for viewing the patient from a solution of zinc bromide. Alternative viewing arrangements include periscopes and closed circuit television.

RADIOISOTOPE DEPARTMENTS

There are two main sections in radioisotope departments and their protection problems need to be approached rather differently. Radioactive sealed sources that are inserted into patients present a problem of storage and handling, as there is an external radiation hazard. They must also be checked for any break of the seal using a wipe test. Radioisotopes in solution are generally of relatively low activity and are of minor storage and external radiation hazard, but present an important problem when handled because of the risk of ingestion and subsequent internal irradiation of critical organs.

Sealed Sources

In a large radiotherapy department using radium, caesium-137 and possibly cobalt-60 in various forms of interstitial and intracavity therapy, there may be several curies of active isotopes. Thus some form of radiation barrier is necessary to reduce the dose rate when the isotopes are not in use. This can be combined with a distance effect by having the area in which the needles and tubes are manipulated between the storage drawers and the lead barrier (see fig. 7-3). It is important to note that there must be lead under the active sources during storage and manipulation. For the conditions shown in the figure,

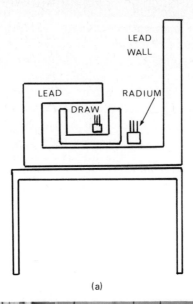

(a)

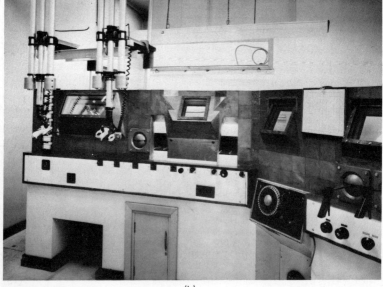

(b)

Fig. 7.3. (a) A bench for handling sealed sources. (b) Radium Lab. R. V. I. Newcastle on Tyne showing remote handling equipment.

where the barrier is a total thickness of 6-inch lead and the distance is 100 cm, the dose rate just beyond the barrier, if the safe contains one curie of radium, would be about one micro roentgen per hour. Transport of radium and caesium within the hospital is often necessary. Lead-lined trolleys must be used, but these would be unmanageable with too much lead. One inch of lead is adequate for this purpose because the time factors involved are short and the trolley has a long handle to provide a distance factor.

In the theatre the needles and tubes are handled as little as possible, and always with forceps. The best method of reducing dose to theatre staff is the afterloading method of insertion in which dummy sources are introduced in theatre and radiographed to check their position; the active sources can then be quickly introduced when the patient is on the ward. This method requires specially designed flexible holders for the sources and is suitable for intracavity treatment.

Unsealed Sources

Diagnostic doses of radioisotopes have activities of the order of 1/1,000 of treatment quantities. Thus the storage problem is relatively minor. In a busy department however, some degree of shielding is desirable to prevent unnecessary raising of the background level. Many of the more widely used isotopes (^{99m}Tc, ^{113m}In) which have their own generators are already shielded in lead pots.

The Hazard of Ingestion

The hazard of external radiation from diagnostic quantities of radioisotopes is negligible. The main danger comes from ingestion and subsequent concentration in particular organs, particularly from an isotope which emits beta particles. The combined effect of the concentration in an organ, e.g. thyroid gland, and the total absorption of the beta-ray energy within that organ can produce a relatively high dose of radiation from even a very low dose of isotope. In general the dose of the gland depends on:

   (i)   the amount of isotope in the organ,
   (ii) the size of the organ,
   (iii) the energy of the beta rays,

(iv) the rate at which the activity within the organ falls; this is a combination of the physical half-life of the isotope and the biological half-life due to the physiological processes within the organ.

Some typical examples of dose values are:

thyroid 1.5 rad/μCi from Iodine-131
liver 1 rad/μCi from Cobalt-58

Handling of Radioisotopes

During the preparation and dispensing of radioisotopes they should be treated as highly toxic chemicals. Any manipulation should be done with the isotope preferably in solution and behind a perspex or glass barrier to prevent any spray from reaching personnel. The following rules must be observed within the radioisotope laboratory;

(1) pipetting must never be done by mouth,
(2) disposable gloves should be used,
(3) eating, drinking and smoking are forbidden.

There is always the risk of spillage; solutions should be handled on non-absorbent surfaces which can easily be cleaned. In the event of radioactive materials being spilt the following should be easily available:

(a) decontamination fluid—this is basically a strong detergent which will dissolve out any radioactive salt in the surface of a material (it does not neutralise the radioactivity!),
(b) a sensitive radiation detector (G.M. counter or scintillation counter) to determine the site of the contamination and whether improvement is made after washing with decontaminating fluid.

Waste Disposal

Radioactive materials which have decayed beyond a useful activity or items of contaminated apparatus, bottles, gloves, etc. may, separately, be all of low activity, but when put together may add up to an appreciable quantity. A polythene bag full of this waste can be checked in a simple monitoring apparatus to determine the level of activity. If it exceeds the level laid down by the code of practice for the particular isotope, e.g. 10 μCi in three cubic feet if the waste is to be disposed of by public services or 10 mCi by discharge to a public sewer every four weeks, the waste must be stored in a suitable basement room away from personnel until this level of activity is reached.

Protection Instruments

To measure leakage radiation from X-ray and gamma-ray external beam sets and radiation penetrating barriers a portable sensitive dose rate monitor is required. One such instrument (shown in fig. 7-4), which can be calibrated to measure dose rates of the order of mR/hr is a battery operated dosemeter consisting of a large ionisation chamber and direct current amplifier with a meter for direct reading.

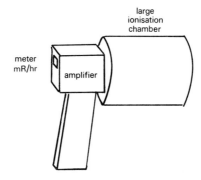

Fig. 7.4. A portable ionisation chamber for area surveys.

To detect radiation rather than accurately measure its intensity a G.M. counter is necessary. The pulses can be made audible by passing them through a loudspeaker as the ear is very sensitive to changes in counting rate.

For assessment of the integrated dose level over several days at a point in a room small films, of the type used in personnel monitoring, can be used.

Personnel Monitoring

The final proof that all protection measures are adequate is given from actually monitoring the dose received by staff. The most common method for long-term monitoring of general body dose is the film badge. Although film should not be used as a dosimeter where accurate radiation measurements (to within a few percent) is required, it is entirely adequate for protection measurement as it provides a useful permanent record of the radiation received over a wide range of dose levels (10 mR-20 R), and if used carefully the dose can be estimated to ±10%.

The main difficulty with film is that the film sensitivity varies with energy; there is generally a large increase in sensitivity as the photon energy decreases below 100 keV. This means that the same blackening of the film can be produced by either 10 mR of 70 kVp X-rays or about 200 mR of Cobalt-60 gamma-rays. To identify the radiation received by the film various filters are used to absorb different radiation by different amounts. One such film may contain the materials shown in fig. 7-5, e.g. if soft X-rays are incident there is very little blackening beneath the tin filter, more beneath the aluminium, and most beneath the open window; if high energy X- or gamma-rays are incident the blackening is similar throughout except for the open window where lack of build-up reduces the dose and therefore the amount of blackening.

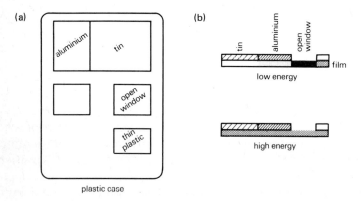

Fig. 7.5. (a) A personnel's monitoring film badge showing the different filters used for determining the quality of radiation received. (b) Shows the blackening of film in case of: (i) low-energy—no blackening beneath tin; (ii) high energy—similar blackening under all absorbers.

CHAPTER 8

The Use of Ultrasonics in Medicine

Ultrasonic diagnostic techniques have now an established place in clinical practice. The basic sound-echo principle to determine the depth of an object by measuring the time taken for a pulse of ultrasound to reach an object and for the reflected wave to arrive back at the detector has been known and used for some time, especially in the charting of the sea-bed. However, it is only relatively recently that the ancillary instrumentation has been developed to allow ultrasonic techniques to be brought into routine use on patients. Transistor circuits have aided this development; future developments in the apparatus associated with ultrasonics will rely on the new range of integrated circuits to perform complex switching, temporary storage of data, etc. that is necessary for obtaining certain images.

Ultrasonics vs. Radiography

Ultrasonic diagnosis is based in most cases on the reflection of part of the ultrasonic energy from an interface within the body. Although this echo may be of low intensity it can be detected by a sensitive receiver and amplified for display. The transmitted wave penetrates deeper into the body and reflections occur at other interfaces. The information concerning structure within the body is thus primarily from these reflections, although sometimes this transmitted wave is used in diagnosis.

Radiography uses information obtained from the transmission of X-rays. Ultrasonics will not take the place of radiography; they are complementary tools of diagnosis. With X-rays a three-dimensional object is imaged on to a two-dimensional film from which defects at particular sites can be an aid to diagnosis. This requires the natural radiographic contrast of, for example, bone/soft-tissue, or the artificially introduced contrast of a barium meal to allow the radiologist to perceive the defect. At its most sophisticated X-radiography can provide a three-dimensional cross-section picture by the analysis of multiple two-dimensional images. This is of use in special diagnosis of the brain. Ultrasonics can produce a cross-sectional picture of a patient without any complex analysis, because it can detect and display the interfaces between different tissues. These interfaces need not necessarily be between tissues of different densities; only the structure of the medium need change for a reflection to occur. Thus unlike radiography, soft tissues of different types, e.g. connective tissue and liver tissue, or the fluid within a soft tissue surround can be visualised directly.

The main advantage of diagnostic ultrasound is that its use appears to be of no hazard to the patient and there are no immediate or long-term effects. The unfortunate aspect of the use of radiography (ionising radiation) is its very small, but undeniable, long-term effect on a proportion of the population. It was a long time before the long-term radiation hazard of ionising radiations was recognised and users of ultrasound must always be aware of the possibility of such a long-term effect.

Matter Waves

Although sound waves are frequently referred to in terms of radiation, it must be remembered that it is a propagation of energy through a medium (see fig. 8-1); the medium itself does not generally move in the direction of this propagation. The energy is transported as a result of the transmission of an oscillation from one particle to the next; these particles oscillate at right-angles to the direction of energy propagation. One of the best illustrations of this is the waves formed when a stone is

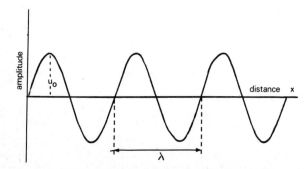

Fig. 8.1. A sine wave of amplitude u_0 and wavelength λ. If moving to right $u = u_0 \sin [w(t - x/c)]$ where w is angular frequency, c is the velocity of wave so that $c = f\lambda$.

dropped into a flat calm pond or lake which has leaves on its surface. The ripples spread out at a definite velocity and as each ripple reaches a leaf it lifts it vertically and passes on without moving the leaf in the direction of spread.

The lower frequency limit of the ultrasonic spectrum is generally taken to be about 20 kHz (the majority of the population cannot hear sound above this frequency); however, the frequencies suitable for most diagnostic applications are in the range 1-15 MHz.

Ultrasonic Generation

Matter waves suitable for diagnostic ultrasound must have frequencies in the range 1-10 MHz, and be of sufficient power so that pulse echo techniques can be used. For this frequency range and power level ultrasound is produced by the piezo-electric effect. This effect occurs in certain crystals (e.g. quartz) when they are subjected to a high electric field of several hundred volts per millimetre, which causes the crystal to distort. Crystals of quartz were used on early record players which utilised the reverse effect of mechanical distortion of the crystal producing an electrical signal across the crystal. Both these properties are used in diagnostic ultrasound transducers. If a high-frequency electrical signal is applied to a crystal a certain amount of the energy will be converted into ultrasound; when an ultrasound beam is incident on such a crystal, the sound energy will be converted into an electrical signal. The magnitude of these effects for piezoelectric crystals are measured by: the transmission coefficient, d, which is the strain produced per unit electric field; and the receiving coefficient, g, which is the electric field produced per unit stress. The most commonly used transducer material in ultrasonic diagnosis is the synthetic ceramic lead zirconate titanate. These piezoelectric ceramics are known as ferroelectrics; they are polarised during manufacture by applying an electric field of about 20 kV per cm across the ceramic when it has been heated to a temperature above its curie point, then slowly cooled. For a particular commercial ferroelectric, PZT-4[1] the value of the transmission coefficient is 289×10^{-12} m/volt, or about 0.3 μm/kV; the reception coefficient is 2.61×10^{-2} volt $\cdot$ m/newton.

When alternating voltage is applied to the surfaces of one of

[1] Brush Crystal Co. Ltd.

these transducers in the form of a disc, oscillations are set up within the disc. Some of this oscillatory energy will pass into the medium immediately in contact with the crystal, however, at the surface of the disc some energy will be reflected back. If the frequency of the applied voltage and the thickness of the disc are such that the reflected wave reinforces the next expansion of the disc the transducer is said to be operating in its resonant condition. This is the most efficient state of operation of such a transducer and is used when continuous wave operation is required. For the ferroelectric mentioned above a disc of 2 mm thickness will resonate at 1 MHz. This thickness corresponds to value of half a wavelength in this material.

Pulse Response

High frequency matter waves for most diagnostic uses (except Doppler-shift techniques) are produced by exciting a piezo-electric crystal with the sudden application of an electrical pulse from a circuit such as that shown in fig. 8-2. This makes the crystal "ring" at its natural frequency. The length of the transmitted pulse depends on the amount of damping of the oscillation by the materials surrounding the crystal. For the most efficient transmission of energy there should be as little damping as possible. However, the very pulsed nature of the

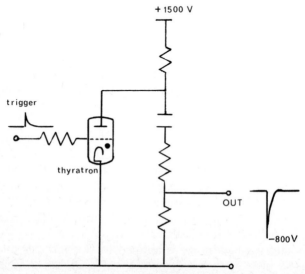

Fig. 8.2. An H.T. pulse generating circuit.

transmitted pulse means that the signal contains a range of frequencies; thus to detect the reflected signals the crystal must have a reasonably flat response over a range of frequencies. This is achieved by backing the transducer with a highly absorbing material, see fig. 8-3, to dampen the pulse.

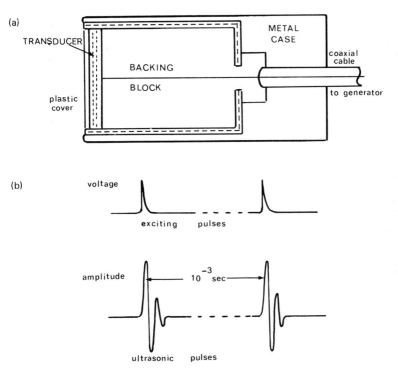

Fig. 8.3. (a) An ultrasonic probe (after Wells). (b) The ultrasonic pulses (p.r.f. = 1000 Hz) produced by transient impulses containing oscillations at the natural frequency of the transducer.

The Ultrasonic Beam from a Disc Transducer
The mathematical models of the propagation of sound waves use wave theory in the same way as the wave theories of light (e.g. Huygens' principle). For a disc-shaped transducer the theory is analogous to the propagation of light through a slit. This produces two zones in which the intensity varies in distinctly different patterns.

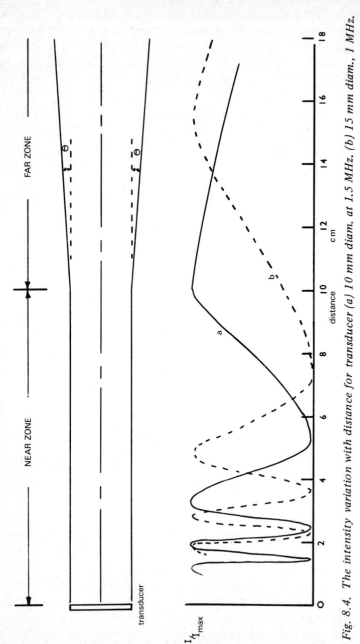

Fig. 8.4. The intensity variation with distance for transducer (a) 10 mm diam. at 1.5 MHz. (b) 15 mm diam., 1 MHz.

The Near (Fresnel) Zone

Close to the transducer the steady-state intensity varies in an oscillatory fashion depending on the distance from the transducer along the axis (see fig. 8-4). This is associated with the interference pattern which produces rings of high and low intensity alternately across the beam. The interference pattern itself is not of much importance in pulse echo techniques, but the position of the end of this near zone is of interest. This is determined by the position of the last intensity maximum which occurs at:

$$x_{max} = \frac{4r^2 - \lambda^2}{4\lambda};$$

r = diameter of transducer, λ = wavelength of radiation,

or if

$$r^2 \gg \lambda^2 \text{ then } x_{max} = \frac{r^2}{\lambda}.$$

Thus the higher the frequency the shorter the wavelength and the deeper the end of the near zone; e.g. for a wavelength of 1.5 mm and $r = 15$ mm, $x_{max} = 150$ mm.

The Far (Fraunhofer) Zone

In the near field the beam is of reasonably constant diameter and therefore, excluding any absorption effects, the intensity is almost constant. In the far field, however, the beam begins to diverge with a half-angle given by: $\sin \theta = 0.61 \lambda/r$. For the above conditions, the half-angle would be about 0.06 radians, or 3.5 degrees.

This divergence means a reduction in intensity as the same flux passes through a greater area. If beam uniformity is desired to a greater depth, a focusing transducer can be used which effectively extends the range of the near zone. Focusing can be achieved in a similar fashion to light focusing—except that the source of radiation is not a point—e.g. a plane transducer can be used with an ultrasonic lens. Polystyrene or perspex are used as lens materials (fig. 8-5), with the lens a concave shape to produce a convergent beam, unlike the light analogy. It is also possible to produce concave-shaped transducers in ceramic materials with a fixed focus distance.

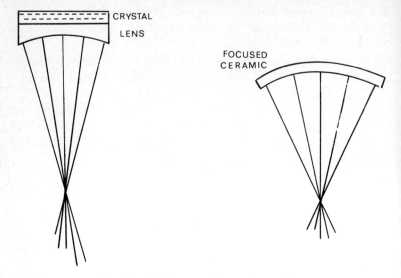

Fig. 8.5. Two types of focused transducer.

Attenuation and Absorption of the Ultrasonic Beam

Sound waves in a medium cause rapid variations in local pressure levels; in general these pressure waves have properties depending on their frequency. In most applications of ultrasonic techniques these waves are transmitted in a linear fashion, i.e. in a longitudinal mode, by the transfer of oscillations from one volume element to the next; these oscillations being at right-angles to the direction of propagation of the beam. The ease with which these vibrations can be transferred depends directly on the elasticity of the medium, K, and inversely on the density, ρ, the more dense the medium the less easily the volume elements can be made to vibrate. It can be shown that the velocity of a pressure wave through a medium: $c = (K/\rho)^{1/2}$, e.g. for water, $c = 1{,}500 \text{ ms}^{-1}$. Soft tissue and body fluids have similar values to this, but compact bone, although more dense, has a value: $c = 4{,}000 \text{ ms}^{-1}$, because of its higher elasticity. The basic equation relating velocity and frequency of a waveform is $c = f\lambda$; thus at a typical ultrasonic frequency for diagnostic applications, $f = 1$ MHz, the wavelength is 1.5 mm in soft tissue. This value immediately gives us some idea of the resolving power of diagnostic ultrasound (see section on resolution below).

Attenuation

The intensity of a beam of constant energy flux is determined by the beam area; if the beam is broadened the same flux passes through a greater area and the intensity is reduced. In the ultrasonic field this broadening occurs in the far field where the beam diverges. A certain amount of attenuation occurs also in all parts of the field due to the scattering of the beam by irregularities in the medium.

Absorption

Some of the ultrasonic energy which causes the volume elements of a medium to vibrate is absorbed by the individual atoms or molecules which form the element. These vibrations at the atomic level are random in nature and do not assist the

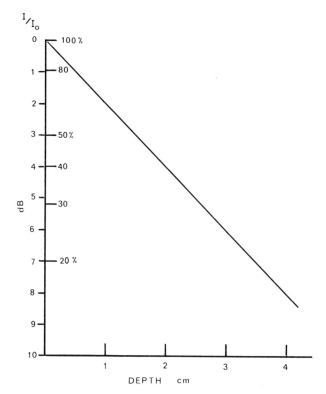

Fig. 8.6. *An absorption curve showing the relationship between dB and percentage transmission.*

transmission of the energy at the macroscopic level, so useful energy is lost to the medium in the form of heat. This absorption of energy follows an exponential law (fig. 8-6), i.e. the rate of loss of energy depends on the intensity at that point. It follows that a constant proportion of energy is removed from the beam when it passes through equal thicknesses of medium; the intensity beyond a given thickness of absorber is thus related to the incident intensity by the equation: $I = I_0\ e^{-\alpha t}$; where α is the absorption coefficient of the medium. This equation may be more conveniently expressed in the form:

$$\log_e \frac{I}{I_0} = -\alpha t, \qquad \text{or} \qquad 2.3 \log_{10} \frac{I}{I_0} = -\alpha t.$$

For the diagnostic range of ultrasonic frequencies (1-10 MHz) the absorption coefficient in most soft tissues is approximately proportional to frequency, in bone the dependence on frequency is of a higher order. Thus although the higher frequencies have the advantage of a deeper near zone and so less attenuation due to divergence of the beam, this advantage is outweighed by the greater absorption.

Degree of Absorption—the Decibel

Ultrasonic radiation is a propagation of energy and so can be measured in terms of energy flow, e.g. joules per sec. Ultrasonic intensity is the energy flow through unit area in unit time, e.g. joules $\sec^{-1}$ cm^{-2}.

When considering the absorption of ultrasound we are more concerned with a ratio of intensities than with the absolute intensity. In both sound and ultrasound a logarithmic ratio is used to express the change in intensity level as this allows many orders of magnitude to be expressed simply. The most common unit of intensity change (n.b. a dimensionless unit) is the decibel defined as:

$$\text{Intensity ratio} = 10 \log_{10} \frac{I}{I_0} \text{ decibel.}$$

If we let $\alpha' = 10\alpha/2.3$ in the equation relating intensity and absorption coefficient, it can be seen that the absorption coefficient can be expressed in terms of $dB \cdot cm^{-1}$. For example, if 5 cm of material reduce the intensity by 10 dB the absorption coefficient is $2\ dB \cdot cm^{-1}$.

Reflection at Interface

When an ultrasonic beam meets a boundary between two media some of the incident energy will be reflected; it is this reflected energy which is detected and used in most diagnostic applications. The amount of energy reflected depends on the difference between the two media. This difference is measured in terms of the characteristic impedances of the media.

Characteristic Impedance

It can be shown that the instantaneous particle pressure produced by a matter wave is given by: $p = \rho c v$; where v is the particle velocity. Because of the similarity with the basic equation in electricity, the quantity ρc is designated the characteristic impedance of the medium; it is a measure of the ability of the medium to transmit ultrasound waves. The characteristic impedance of air is thus very much less than that of soft-tissue because of the large density difference.

Reflection at a Plane Interface

In most pulse echo diagnostic systems it is usual to have the same transducer acting as both transmitter and receiver; this restricts the surfaces from which echoes can be received to those which are normal to the beam, so only the reflection at a plane interface will be considered. If the interface is of sufficiently large dimension compared to the wavelength of the ultrasound (1.5 mm/MHz) a proportion of the radiation will be reflected and the rest transmitted depending on the type of media at the interface. It can be shown that the intensity reflection coefficient:

$$\frac{I_r}{I_i} = \frac{(Z_2 - Z_1)^2}{(Z_2 + Z_1)},$$

I_i = incident intensity, I_r = reflected intensity, Z_1 = characteristic impedance of first medium, Z_2 = characteristic impedance of second medium. There are two conditions of special interest: (i) if $Z_1 = Z_2$ there is no reflection, (ii) if $Z_2 \ll Z_1$ nearly all the incident energy is reflected. An example of the latter case is the tissue/air interface; the lack of energy penetrating beyond such an interface makes it very difficult to visualise the lung fields.

PULSE ECHO SYSTEMS

The A-Scope

The basic elements of the A-scope are shown in the fig. 8-7. It is essentially a device for determining depth by timing the reflections of pulses of ultrasound from interfaces. The display, the A-scan, shows a number of voltage pulses at various distances along the screen corresponding to different types of interface at various positions within the body. The method of production of this trace is as follows: (i) the power supply to the transducer produces pulses at a rate determined by the rate generator; (ii) each pulse of ultrasound travels through the patient producing echoes at each interface between different media; (iii) the transducer detects those echoes from interfaces at right-angles to the beam; (iv) the small electrical signal produced at the transducer by an echo signal is amplified (see fig. 8-8) and displayed on the oscilloscope screen; (v) these signals appear at time intervals depending on the depth of the interface; thus the position along the X-axis of the screen determines the depth of an interface, if the system has been calibrated correctly. Since the transducer acts both as transmitter and receiver

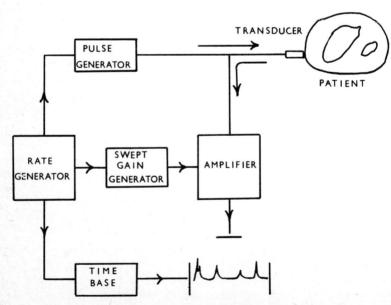

Fig. 8.7. A schematic diagram of the operation of the A scope.

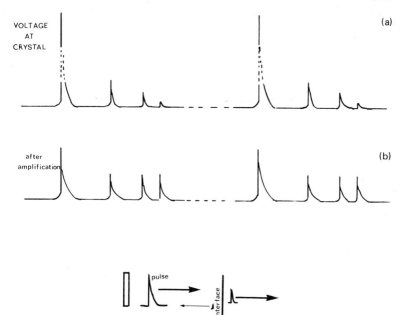

Fig. 8.8. Showing (a) how the intensity of the reflected pulses de-creases with distance and (b) how this is compensated by swept gain amplification.

the pulse repetition frequency must be chosen to allow for this. The transducer must be able to act as a receiver for the length of time it takes for the transmitted pulse to reach the greatest depth required for echoes to return to the transducer from this depth. In soft tissue, where the velocity of ultrasound is approximately 1,500 ms^{-1} the transmitted pulse takes approximately 200 μs to travel 30 cm, so the p.r.f. must be no more than 2,500 Hz. In practice repetition frequencies up to 1,000 Hz are used.

Resolution

The resolution of any radiation probe system is ultimately limited by the wavelength of the radiation. In the case of diagnostic ultrasound with frequencies in the range 1-10 MHz the wavelength is 1.5 to 0.15 mm; however, because the transducer emits a spectrum of frequencies the true resolution is generally poorer than the theoretical resolution. For example the best resolution possible at 2 MHz is of the order of 2-3 mm. This applies to the depth of an object only. Lateral resolution depends on the width of the beam which varies with distance from the transducer. In general the lateral resolution depends on the width of the transducer and the intensity pattern it produces in the absorbing medium; it must therefore be measured in terms of the beam width necessary at a given range to produce a detectable echo from a point source.

THE USE OF THE A-SCAN

Midline Echo Encephalography

One of the first uses of diagnostic ultrasound is the valuable technique of determining the position of the median saggital plane with respect to the true midline of the brain. This gives an indication as to whether the midline structures have been displaced laterally by a cerebral disorder; this is especially useful in emergencies involving the head in which continuing bleeding in one hemisphere may cause increasing deformity of the midline structures.

To perform the test the ultrasonic probe is placed on the scalp 2-3 cm above and just anterior to the external auditory

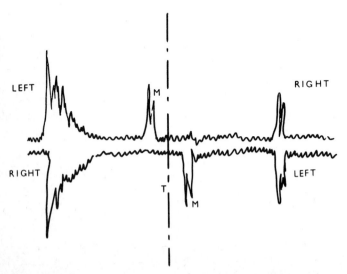

Fig. 8.9. Echoencephalograms from right and left sides of head show: M—midline echoes; T—true midline determined from transmission measurement.

meatus. The transducer is coupled to the scalp to prevent any reflecting air space by using a suitable light oil or vaseline. The midline structures give rise to a high amplitude echo, called the M echo. The picture produced on the oscilloscope screen is photographed with polaroid film and the distance of the M echo from each surface echo of the scalp is measured. These distances are compared with the true semi-diameter of the head. It is more accurate to use two transducers to obtain two sets of information on the reflected and transmitted beams (fig. 8-9), so that all the measurements are made electronically.

Uses in Ophthalmology

As the eye is a small structure useful detail can only be seen with good resolution. Thus higher frequencies than usual must be used, for example, a frequency of 20 MHz gives a resolution of about 0.07 mm. To avoid the confusing complex of signals which appears at the beginning of an A-scan it is useful to use a short water-filled cylinder as a viewing box; this also enables good contact between transducer and the eye to be made easily.

Biparietal Cephalometry

A most useful measurement in obstetrics which can be performed without any harm to the foetus, is the biparietal diameter. This can give an indication of the maturity of the foetus and, if made regularly during a critical period, can indicate whether growth has been retarded by placental insufficiency or is continuing at a reasonable rate. The average growth rate in the last ten weeks of pregnancy appears to be about 0.17 cm per week. A good technique involves identifying the head using a B-scan system and placing the probe so that it is passing through the widest diameter before switching to an A-scan to measure the diameter accurately.

The B-Scope

Instead of displaying the pulse echo information as a series of pulse amplitudes, it can be displayed as a line of dots with the same spacing along the axis as the A-scan but with a brightness depending on the amplitude of the echo (fig. 8-10). This allows the coordinates of an interface to be built up on the oscilloscope screen as the ultrasonic beam can be directed from different angles; the resulting picture is known as the B-scan. Provision must be made for the beam direction through the

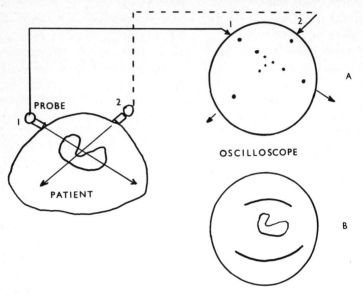

Fig. 8.10. *The basic principle of 2-dimensional scanning (B-scan) showing: (a) brightness modulated echoes for two beam directions along same direction on screen; (b) the compound scan.*

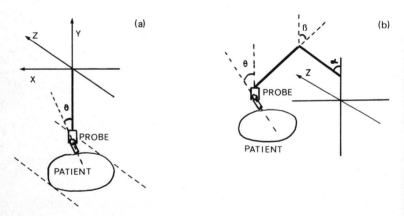

Fig. 8.11. *Two-dimensional scans coordinate systems. (a) Rectilinear scans in X-Y plane with the possibility of shift movement along the Z axis. (b) Polar coordinates. It is also possible to tilt plane of scanning from vertical.*

patient to be transferred to the display so that the echoes appear along a baseline corresponding to this direction; this allows the picture to be built up automatically. The vital feature of such an instrument is the accurate conversion of the mechanical movements of the probe into electrical signals suitable for the deflecting coils in an oscilloscope. This is achieved by potentiometers of high accuracy so that a feature within the body produces an echo at the same place on the screen for any beam direction.

Various systems are used by different commercial instruments. Most are constrained to allow a two-dimensional vertical cross-section of the body to be obtained by manually moving the probe around the patient's contour. The position of the probe is then located electronically in rectilinear or polar coordinates (see fig. 8-11). Since the direction of the beam can also be altered these systems have four degrees of freedom. Some systems also allow tilting of the scan plane out of the vertical thus giving a fifth degree of freedom.

Contact Scanning

The echoes are received by the scanning head only if the interface of interest is normal to the beam of ultrasound. The organs of the body, however, are not only curved but may have very uneven surfaces, thus to obtain the greatest amount of information from the outline of an interface the probe must be rocked as it is moved round the body (fig. 8-12). This is quite a skilful operation as the transducer must be kept in intimate contact with the skin; any air space will totally reflect the ultrasound before it can enter the body. The movement of the transducer is eased by a film of oil smeared on the patient's skin which also provides the required coupling between transducer and skin. This system of scanning is very suitable on the soft structures of the abdomen, e.g. liver, placenta and foetus, urinary tract.

Rectilinear Scanning

For very soft structures contact scanning is not satisfactory particularly for the breast where information close to the skin is required. In these cases a water bath can be used to enclose the volume to be scanned and then automatic linear scanning can be used to produce a B-scan along any required section of the

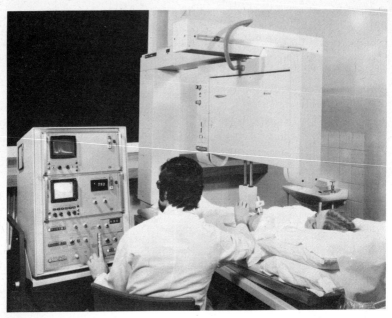

Fig. 8.12. Diasongraph NE4102 Ultrasonic scanner (courtesy of Nuclear Enterprises Ltd).

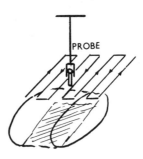

Fig. 8.13. Rectilinear scanning at constant depth. Patient must be in waterbath or under water bag.

volume (see fig. 8-13). Alternatively a definite scanning depth can be chosen by using electronic gates to remove pulses before and after a given time interval which corresponds to the required depth. The scan is performed in a rectilinear fashion. In either of these systems information is lost if a structure is not at right angles to the beam. It is possible to improve the image by rocking the transducer to alter the beam angle.

Recording of the B-Scan

There are two basic recording methods: (i) by photographing the dots with a high-speed film, e.g. polaroid, as they arrive on a short persistence phosphor oscilloscope screen; (ii) by allowing the whole image to be displayed on a storage oscilloscope on which the image is stored electrically for up to several minutes. The image that is finally chosen can then be photographed for a permanent record. Each system has its advantages: the short persistence method produces a grey scale which allows more information to be stored; the storage oscilloscope allows many pictures to be formed and destroyed in rapid succession, and a permanent record need only be made of the best result.

USES OF THE B-SCAN

Obstetrics and Gynaecology

The abdomen is a very convenient part of the body for direct contact B-scanning as there are no bony structures to interfere by absorbing the beam. In early pregnancy it is even possible to

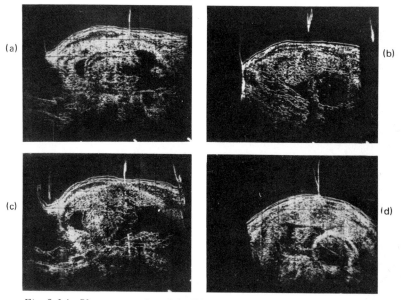

Fig. 8.14. Placentography. (a), (b), (c) longitudinal and (d) transverse scans of breech presentation of foetus. (c) Shows the symphesis pubis marked (on the left) with a full bladder lying immediately below, the placenta lies mainly anteriorly but part of it is next to the bladder; (d) shows the head and mid-line of head (Dept. Med. Phys. Newcastle General Hospital).

observe the gestation sac within the uterus as early as five to seven weeks by scanning longitudinally through a full bladder which acts as a viewing chamber as it displaces the intestines. This makes it possible to diagnose a pregnancy which is not developing normally.

In later pregnancy the diagnosis of the position of the foetus can be made positively and quickly. Placentography can be achieved without the small but not insignificant hazard introduced by radioisotope localisation of the placenta (fig. 8-14).

Liver
The liver size and consistency can be found by scanning over the abdomen during inspiration at an angle from the vertical so as to pass through the greatest diameter of the liver. The greatest value of the liver scan is in the diagnosis of cysts and abscesses within the liver, but it can also be of use for the identification of primary and secondary tumours if used in conjunction with data from other tests.

The Urinary Tract
The kidney size and position can be found from a B-scan of the posterior abdominal wall. Bladder volume can be measured accurately and in certain cases the echo patterns can be used to clinically stage bladder tumours.

Ophthalmology
Water-bath scanners are used in ophthalmological investigations. Water type coupling to the patient's eye may be achieved by means of a plastic sheet cemented to the face with the patient supine. With frequencies 10-20 MHz an anatomical pattern is produced with range and lateral resolution, with a small enough probe, of 0.2-0.3 mm. This type of investigation is especially useful where optical instruments cannot be used due to the presence of cataracts.

Time-Position Recording
In the majority of cases a B-scan can be produced in a sufficiently short time so that the structures being imaged will have only moved slightly, if at all. However, there is one important organ, the heart, which contains rapidly moving parts that are seen as pulsating movements on the B-scan which would blur any image. It is possible to record these movements

by various techniques based on the system shown in fig. 8-15. The probe remains stationary; the B-scan is moved as a whole across the Y-axis of the screen producing a line pattern corresponding to the movement of the position of a pulse echo. This pattern can be seen on a storage scope display or it can be recorded on film.

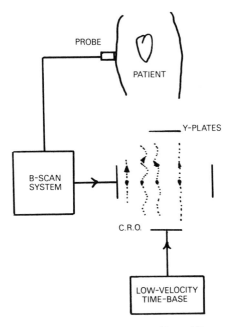

Fig. 8.15. Time position recording of B-scan.

Mitral Valve Movement

The above technique can be used to assess mitral valve function. However, an ultrasonic beam passing through the heart produces a large number of moving echoes which cause confusion. It is possible to pick out the movement of the mitral valve only, by discriminating electronically against signals from other structures. An electronic gate is closed to those echoes which always occur before the arrival of the echo of interest. The time between the opening of this gate and the arrival of the echo is converted to a voltage proportional to the time interval. Thus the variations in the position of the structure causing the echo can be recorded as voltage analogues directly on a chart recorder. The system is known as a time-to-voltage analogue converter.

Array Scanning

There is another method of viewing the movement of structures of the heart. An array of some twenty individual transducers within a single linear head is directed at the heart. The B-scan from each transducer is displayed on an oscilloscope. The changing patterns are then recorded on film.

THE DOPPLER EFFECT IN ULTRASONICS

When a wave motion is associated with a moving source there is a change in frequency of the radiated wave. This is particularly noticeable with sound waves, for example, if a car sounds its horn while passing a stationary observer the pitch of the note appears to change from high to low. In fact the frequency changes by a definite amount depending on the velocity of the source. If the nominal frequency is f the change in frequency experienced by a stationary observer is $\pm vf/c$; where v is the velocity of the source and the positive sign refers to objects moving towards the observer, the negative sign refers to the source moving away from the observer, c is the velocity of sound and v is very much less than c.

This frequency shift can be utilised in ultrasonics in the quantitative study of moving structures. If the Doppler shift in frequency of a continuous wave ultrasonic beam reflected from a moving object is measured, the velocity of the object can be calculated. In this case the frequency shift is $2vf/c$, so that for a 2 MHz ultrasonic beam with a velocity in soft tissue of 1,500 m/s the shift in frequency is 26 Hz per cm/sec., i.e. 260 Hz for an object moving at 10 cm/sec. In practice the signal received from the body contains the nominal frequency due to waves reflected from stationary surfaces and Doppler shifted frequencies from a moving structure. All the signals are received by the transducer. They can be processed by demodulation and filtration to obtain the Doppler shifted signals only.

Clinical Use

Blood flow in vessels can be detected using this method (see section in chapter on physiological measurement). In cardiology the Doppler technique can be used for the detection of the timing of the heart valves.

TREATMENT USING ULTRASOUND
At sufficiently high levels of intensity using continuous wave ultrasound, enough energy can be concentrated into a small volume to cause damage to tissue. This directional beam of ultrasound can be used as a precision surgical tool.

The Instrument
The probes used are very different from the diagnostic probes, although the principle of generation of ultrasound is the same. One particular transducer is a quartz crystal of about 4 cm diameter excited by 3.5 kV oscillations at 1 MHz. The ultrasonic vibration of the crystal is coupled via liquid to a metal cone. The cone converges the ultrasonic beam to an area of 0.2 cm^2. The intensity at the end of the cone is of the order of 10 watts/cm^2.

CLINICAL USE
Treatment of Ménière's Disease
Ménière's disease is a disease of the inner ear causing unpleasant attacks of dizziness and vomiting due to an imbalance of pressure within the semicircular canals. The surgical operation to cure this destroys hearing; the basis of ultrasound treatment is to irradiate the semicircular canal precisely after surgical exposure. The nerve that transmits balance information to the brain is destroyed without affecting hearing.

Parkinson's Disease
This is a disease of the central nervous system causing rigidity of limbs and unsteadiness of gait. Destruction of certain small volumes of tissue deep in the brain has been found to relieve the symptoms. The advantage of ultrasound is that it can be focused on a small volume without affecting too greatly the intervening and surrounding tissue. However, initial surgery is necessary as part of the skull must be removed to allow the passage of ultrasound into the brain without the large attenuation that bone produces. Sterile liquid is used to couple the

transducer to the brain; focal intensities of 400-1,200 watt/cm^2 are used.

Measurement of Total Power

It is necessary when considering the possible hazard of ultrasound to know the power output of the transducer. An absolute method of determining this uses calorimetry to measure the energy absorbed in a body in which the ultrasonic beam is completely absorbed. Thermistors are used to measure the temperature rise, although these are very sensitive, with typical changes in resistance of the order of 5%/°C, at least 100 mW is needed if an accurate measurement is to be made.

An alternative method is to use the force produced by the ultrasound to deflect an accurate balance; this deflection is directly related to the total power of the beam. Unfortunately although simple in principle this is a difficult measurement in practice for the following reasons: (i) the measurement must be made in water, (ii) the ultrasonic waves must be totally absorbed by the balance, i.e. there must be no transmission, (iii) the balance must be very sensitive. Balances capable of this measurement have been developed, with a sensitivity of the order of 100 mg/cm deflection for 1 watt of power, using for example torsion wires to eliminate friction and an absorber at 45° to the ultrasonic beam to absorb and reflect the beam without transmission. Such a system is calibrated using weights and correcting for their buoyancy.

To study the distribution of intensity across an ultrasonic beam it is necessary to use a small detector, in which case a power level of 1 watt/cm^2 is necessary at 1 MHz to give sufficient sensitivity. A qualitative picture of intensity distribution across the beam may be found using Schlieren optics. As an ultrasound beam passes through water the oscillations within the water change its refractive index. The water can thus be used as an optical defraction grating which is used to display an image of the intensity distribution on a photograph.

Power Levels

As has already been mentioned the power levels in ultrasound therapy can be of the order of several hundred watts/cm^2. A typical diagnostic ultrasound beam has a mean intensity of about 2 mW. If the repetition frequency is 1 kHz and each pulse is about 0.5 μs long the maximum intensity is of the order of 4 watts.

The Hazard of Ultrasound

Ultrasonic energy is absorbed in tissue by three different processes: (i) true absorption, i.e. the transfer of energy to the molecule causing it to vibrate in various modes resulting in the release of thermal energy, (ii) scattering—this arises from changes in acoustic impedance of a medium where the discontinuity has dimensions of the order of the wavelength of ultrasound, (iii) cavitation—all liquids contain sub-microscopic bubbles of gas which can grow in size when subjected to changes in pressure. When these bubbles grow to a certain size in relation to the ultrasonic wavelength they behave as resonant cavities and so vibrate with larger amplitude than the surrounding structures. This can lead to effects that damage tissue, one of these is the production of free radicals.

At sufficiently high intensities ultrasound has a destructive effect due to its absorption by tissue. The mean intensity at the diagnostic level is about 1/1,000 of that used for treatment, and even though the intensity of each pulse is similar to the therapy level there is no observable damage to tissue at this level. In the considerable use of diagnostic ultrasound over twenty years no harmful effects have been reported, however, the possibility of long-term effects must not yet be dismissed.

CHAPTER 9

Physics and Audiology

THE ANATOMY OF THE EAR

It is usual to consider the ear in three separate parts: the outer, middle, and inner ear (fig. 9-1). The outer ear consists of the external receiving section, the pinna, and the passage known as the auditory meatus. The oscillation in this air-space from a sound wave causes vibrations of the eardrum, which is the first part of the middle ear. This section of tightly drawn skin has an area of about 50 mm^2. To the inner side of the skin is attached the first of the chain of three little bones or ossicles, the malleus (or hammer). The oval base of the stapes (or stirrup) fits into the oval window of the cochlea which has an area 3 mm^2. The ossicular bones increase the efficiency of transmission to the inner ear. The middle ear is a cavity completely enclosed except for a connection through the eustacian tube to the pharynx. This tube is normally closed, but if an inequality of pressure

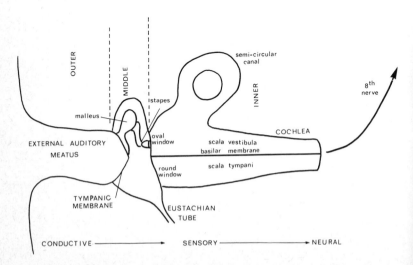

Fig. 9.1. A simplified anatomy of the ear in which the cochlea has been straightened out.

develops across the eardrum, as happens for example in a rapid aeroplane descent, swallowing or yawning will open the tube to equalise the pressure difference. The inner ear contains the cochlea, which is the principal organ, as it converts mechanical signals into electrical impulses; it also contains the apparatus which is used to determine the vertical, the semi-circular canals. The whole of the inner ear is filled with fluid, perilymph, and surrounded by rigid bony walls. When the stapes is pressed into the oval window the pressure is transferred, since liquids are virtually incompressible, through the scarla vestibuli, across the basilar membrane to the scarla tympanum and returns to the round window. The basilar membrane carries the vital structure for sensing operations, the organ of Corti. This organ carries hair cells—many thousands of them of different lengths—and it is the relative movement of these hairs which stimulates nerve fibres. There are roughly the same number of nerve fibres as hair cells. They leave the cochlea grouped in the auditory nerve according to frequency, as different groups of hairs respond to different frequencies.

Sensitivity of the Ear
As with any electrical or mechanical device containing impedances and reactances the ear has two types of response depending whether the stimulation is transient or steady: the transient response is dependent on the rate of growth of the stimulus, the steady-state response is only dependent on the amplitude of the stimulus. Thus in any determination of the sensitivity of the ear, aimed at narrowly defined regions of the ear, it is necessary to use pulses of pure tones which are not suddenly applied to the ear but contain a gradual rise and fall with a pulse length of about one second.

Minimal Audible Pressure
The normal subject's response to sound waves of different frequencies can be seen in fig. 9-2. The curve shows the threshold level of hearing for the different frequencies. The intensity levels are given in terms of dB referred to a sound pressure of 2×10^{-5} N/m^2 (0.0002 dyne/cm^2), which is the normal minimal pressure necessary to produce a response at 3,000 Hz, it corresponds to an energy level of 1.55×10^{-17} watt/cm^2. The ear is most sensitive at this frequency; although the length of the cochlea from the oval to the round window

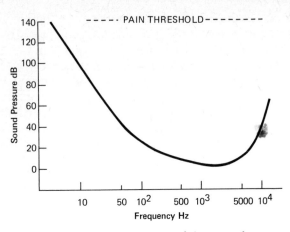

Fig. 9.2. The response curve of the normal ear.

(70 mm) would suggest that it would show resonance at about 10,000 Hz, the velocity of transmission through the cochlea is reduced by the viscous forces acting due to the small diameter of the canals.

The Threshold of Feeling
At high intensities the nervous system of the ear responds differently producing a tickling or pricking sensation. The level of intensity at which this occurs varies only slightly with frequency; this is because the threshold is difficult to measure precisely as it depends on the criteria used.

Loudness and Pitch
These are both subjective qualities, which refer to the parameters of intensity and frequency of the sound wave. The difficulty that a subject has in determining whether two tones have the same loudness can be shown by the fact that if a subject is asked to balance the intensity of a pure tone signal of 100 Hz against a second tone of 1,000 Hz the standard deviation of the difference in intensity can be ±10 dB. Pitch is closely related to frequency; however, if the frequency of a signal is kept constant, the subject will consider that the pitch varies as the intensity is changed. In music it is the change in pitch at constant intensity which is the relevant parameter. The average person can detect a change of about 1/25 of a semitone, i.e. about ½% change in frequency at 1,000 Hz.

AUDIOMETRY—PURE TONE

Instruments which aim to assess hearing acuity are known as audiometers. The threshold level of the intensity of sound at different frequencies of a sinusoidal wave is determined by pure tone audiometry. These instruments can either use air conduction or bone conduction. A combination of the use of these devices, speech audiometry and other well-established tests allow a decision to be made regarding the patient's hearing ability. The instruments are particularly necessary in order to determine how far the auditory response of any individual departs from the normal. It is essential that any instrument is correctly and frequently calibrated against a standard. In the case of air-conduction audiometry the standard is an artificial ear, for bone-conduction audiometry an artificial mastoid is used.

Components of a Pure Tone Audiometer
Oscillator
   This has a range of frequency, producing electrical signals of sinusoidal waveform either in discrete frequency steps or a continuous range of frequency. These frequency signals must be free from harmonic distortion at the intensities required, this is achieved by careful design of the oscillator.

Attenuator
   An attenuator is needed which will accurately change the power output of the oscillator. This is usually in steps of 5 dB, but smaller intervals are available for more precise testing.

Transducer
   The signal may be presented to the patient by air conduction either from a loudspeaker (free field) or through earphones. The latter method is more usual as it reduces the effects of background noise. The transducer must be a high-grade moving-coil device free of distortion at the frequencies required. It is especially important to investigate the frequency response of an earphone for resonance. In bone-conduction audiometry a moving-iron transducer is used as a much larger mass must be moved. Some means of applying this transducer to the head with a definite pressure is necessary.

Switching

The switching of pulses must be made silently to avoid the "click" effect on the ear due to a transient response which is produced by a sudden application of pressure. The electrical pulse is allowed to build up and decay by passing it through a low-pass filter before it reaches the coil.

Calibration of Audiometers

Air Conduction

The power output from the transmitter which provides the electrical signals to the earphone can be determined, but not the intensity of the signal received at the ear in terms of pressure. This can only be done by coupling the transducer to an artificial ear which is equipped with a microphone of known sensitivity. It is essential that this artificial ear is carefully designed to simulate the average human ear, i.e. so that at all frequencies it presents an acoustic load to the sound wave of the same magnitude as the average human ear.

Bone Conduction

The amount of vibration from a moving-iron transducer can be determined, but the effect on the ear itself is not known. The calibration of these transducers is performed using an artificial mastoid that simulates the average human head in terms of mechanical impedance. The sound waves are detected by a vibration sensor instead of a sound pressure detector as in the artificial ear. This detector cannot be placed between the transducer and the mastoid as it would affect the calibration; so the detector, a piezoelectric crystal, is placed in the body of the artificial mastoid. Here it receives a fraction of the force at the surface, this fraction must be determined by independent means. Although the response of the ear in air-conductional geometry is independent of the means by which the transducer is connected to the ear, in bone-conduction audiometry the response depends on the area of contact and the force of application of the transducer. A standard has been set for these conditions (International Organisation for Standardization, 1968b) that the static force should be 5.4 Newtons and that the area of contact should be 1.75 cm^2.

The Recording of Results

In audiometers used for screening large numbers of subjects in industry the instrument can be self-recording (e.g. Békésy audiometer). Five or six discrete frequencies (e.g. 0.5, 1, 2, 3, 4 and 6 kHz) or a continuous range of frequency is used and the intensity is allowed to vary at the rate of +2.5 dB/s or −2.5 dB/s, and the subject indicates when he hears the signal by pressing a button. A more general diagnostic instrument has more facilities and ranges of frequencies. The testing of a subject is complicated by the psychological aspect of under-standing instructions and responding according to his ability to make a decision; whether he is more willing to say, "yes", when he might be wrong than to be sure he is right. This introduces an error in testing that can cause unreal changes of 15-20 dB in either direction of the threshold level at a given frequency.

The response to the signals near the threshold is not a simple "yes" or "no" response but shows a statistical relationship dependent on the intensity. Over a range of 1-2 dB a subject will show a result which varies according to the level of inten-sity. If pulsed tones are used, at high intensity the pulse will be heard every time, but there comes a point, as the intensity is lowered, at which the subject will only hear a certain percentage of the pulses, even though they are all of the same intensity. Detailed study shows that this response is an S-shaped curve (fig. 9-3). A suitable criterion for determining a precise threshold response is to use the 50% response. With the limited time usually available this complete curve cannot be plotted. In practice it is found satisfactory to define the threshold as that value of sound pressure at which at least two responses are

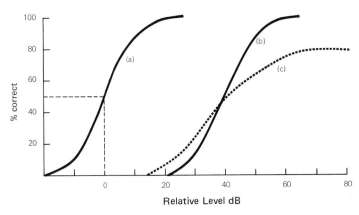

Fig. 9.3. The percentage score in pure tone speech audiometry for (a) normal; (b) conductive deafness; (c) sensorineural deafness.

obtained for four separate stimuli of 2-second duration. This point is approached by first lowering the intensity and then raising it.

The Békésy Audiometer

This has a continuously variable frequency with a range of 100-10,000 Hz. The oscillator is driven by an electric motor over the complete range in 15 minutes. The subject can change the intensity by pressing a button which drives a motor to change an attenuator so that the intensity decreases at about 2.5 dB/min. The subject presses this button for as long as he can hear the test tone then releases it as soon as the tone becomes inaudible. The recording is made automatically, since the motor driving the frequency control also moves a card under a pen-recorder. The resulting audiogram is a zig-zag pattern, but shows the threshold response of the subject.

MASKING

In patients with unilateral hearing loss or asymmetrical bilateral loss there is the possibility of obtaining a false threshold level for the poor ear (T. ear) as the signal may be of such an intensity that it is transmitted across the skull to the non-test ear (N.T. ear). This can produce a false diagnosis. Masking can prevent this and should be used whenever there is any danger of the test tone (in air conduction or bone conduction tests) being heard by the N.T. ear. Masking consists of a noise presented to the N.T. ear to effectively shift its threshold level upwards so that more intense tones can be used on the T. ear without crossover. The masking noise can be one of the following:

(i) complex noise—consisting of a fundamental frequency plus its harmonics;

(ii) white noise—a continuous spectrum of frequency (which can be produced by the device shown in fig. 9-4), but the actual frequencies presented to the ear depend on the frequency response of the transducer; this is usually reasonably flat (±2 dB) up to 6 kHz;

(iii) narrow-band noise—produced by passing a continuous spectrum of frequency through a band-pass filter; the band is described by its centre frequency (e.g. 1 kHz) and band width at −3 dB (e.g. 300 Hz).

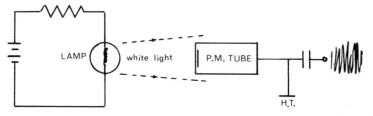

Fig. 9.4. One method of producing white noise.

Narrow-band noise is preferable to white noise, but either should be used instead of complex noise as discrete tones can produce beats with the test tone.

Use of Masking
Masking should be used:

(1) in air-conduction audiometry when the signal presented to the test ear exceeds the bone conduction threshold in the non-test ear by more than 40 dB;

(2) in bone conduction audiometry whenever the test ear exhibits an air-bone gap. In the latter case the procedure would be as follows:

    (i) the air conduction threshold on the N.T. ear is determined using the masking noise,

    (ii) the bone conduction threshold on the T. ear is determined using the pure tone,

    (iii) the masking noise is increased by 10 dB and (ii) repeated.

The apparent threshold for bone conduction of test ear will rise as the masking intensity increases, until the apparent threshold level remains fixed at a value which is the true threshold of the T. ear.

OTHER SUBJECTIVE TESTS

Recruitment of Loudness
This is a term associated with cochlear or perceptive deafness; even if the bone conduction threshold is normal there is recruitment of loudness, i.e. while near the threshold a sound is heard with less than normal loudness, at intensities well above the threshold sounds are heard at normal loudness. The test of

FIXED FREQUENCY 1000 Hz

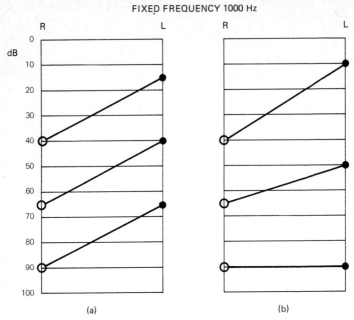

Fig. 9.5. Recruitment of loudness (a) conductive deafness—slope constant; (b) sensori-neural deafness—an increase in slope at lower intensity.

this consists of asking the subject to make loudness adjustments to pure tones of the same frequency applied alternately to each ear. An example of the results of testing is shown in fig. 9-5.

S.I.S.I.

The *short increment sensitivity index* is used in the diagnosis of cochlear disorders. A pure tone is presented to the subject at a certain intensity (about 20 dB above threshold) but punctuated at random intervals by a pulse of $\frac{1}{5}$ second duration at a small increment in intensity level (usually 1 dB), which is imperceptible to the normal ear. However, the subject with loudness recruitment is likely to register this change because of the greater slope of loudness sensation against intensity level. The subject is asked to count the number of pulses he hears. The score is used as a measure of the degree of disorder.

T.T.D.

The *threshold tone decay* is a measure of the degree to which prolonged exposure to a tone produces a loss of sensitivity, so that the intensity of the tone needs to be raised to perceive it. A subject is tested by comparing the effect of a continuous tone against a pulsed tone. Patients suffering from retrocochlear disorders may have normal threshold with pulsed tones, but show dramatic tone decay with the continuous tone. The tone may need to be increased in intensity by up to 60 dB over a two minute exposure in patients with severe disorder.

Speech Audiometry

A speech audiometer is a device for reproducing speech material at known intensity for making tests of articulation or intelligibility. Since the component syllables of speech have a range of intensity of nearly 30 dB it needs careful design to produce a list of syllables and words for a specific purpose. These are recorded on tape and presented to the subject either through earphones or free field. The intensity level during recording is read on a volume indicator (e.g. VU meter) of known response. A plot of the number of words correct (word score) against intensity is made. This has the same S-shape as the curve for pure tones described above (fig. 9-3). The 50% level is taken as the threshold response.

OBJECTIVE TESTS

These are especially useful in subjects who show lack of co-operation in other tests, especially in children.

Evoked Response Audiometry

The response of the patient to auditory stimuli is detected in the E.E.G. The most prominent signals are from the vertex of the scalp (V-potentials, μV in amplitude) in the form of a complex of waves. There are three classes of response depending on the time of appearance after the stimulus:

   (i) fast; with a latency of 8-50 ms,
   (ii) slow; with a latency of 50-300 ms,
   (iii) very slow; with a latency of 300 ms → several seconds.

A computer of average transients (CAT) is used to detect these very low-voltage signals. The CAT operates on the basis of summing many signals and producing their average. This has the effect of increasing the signal/noise ratio, since noise is generally of a random nature and the summation of random signals eventually cancel each other out to zero. The improvement in signal/noise ratio is by a factor of $\sqrt{N}$ where N is the number of responses summed. There must be some means of triggering the averaging system, this is done using a signal from the stimulus generator. The time of averaging is about 500 ms.

Acoustic Impedance Audiometry
The acoustic impedance at the tympanic membrane determines the transmission characteristics of the middle ear. The measurement is performed by varying the pressure on the ear drum (from +200 mm H_2O down to −200 mm H_2O) using a manometer and coupling tube and reflecting sound waves of known intensity off the membrane. The intensity of the reflected waves detected by a microphone can be used to calculate the impedance of the membrane.

The acoustic impedance will show a variation from normal in the following:

(i) lower than normal with ossicular discontinuity,
(ii) higher than normal with clinical otosclerosis,
(iii) very much higher than normal with acute inflammatory and chronic diseases of the middle ear.

Eighth Nerve Action Potential
The action potential of the cochlear nerve is another physiological variable used in objective audiometry. The response to a stimulus is measured using needle electrodes in the nerve, or electrodes on the medullary region; the signal is amplified and the information computer processed as in the evoked response E.E.G. It is hoped that the information from this technique will enable the site of a lesion to be located in the nerve and nuclei which lead from the cochlear up to the brain.

E.M.G. of Post Auricular Muscle
This physiological measurement is monitored for response to auditory stimuli. The signal is again extracted from background noise by computer averaging techniques.

DEFECTS OF HEARING
There are three major classifications of deafness:

(1) Conductive—involving the (mechanical) sound conducting mechanism,
(2) Sensory—involving the cochlea.
(3) Neural—from the 8th nerve to brain.

Conductive Deafness

This may be caused by a simple obstruction of the meatus, or a lesion of the middle ear, or otosclerosis which interferes with movement of the stapes. The subject has a history of relatively good hearing in a noisy environment, but needs to increase the loudness of sound from a radio or television. The results of testing show:

(i) an air-bone gap of magnitude depending on the degree of impairment,

(ii) a speech audiometry threshold which is shifted to right along the intensity scale.

Sensory

Any change in the function of the hair cell and basilar membrane caused by disease or excessive noise produces a sensory defect. The subject has a history of very poor hearing in a noisy environment, poor pitch discrimination, and a low pain threshold. The air-conduction thresholds are similar to those for bone conduction. The subject shows recruitment of loudness and his S.I.S.I. score is high. Speech discrimination scores decrease above the subject's comfortable loudness level.

Neural

This type of deafness may be caused by a lesion of the cells or fibres of the auditory nerve system at any point from the cochlea to the cerebral cortex. The subject has a history of poor hearing in a noisy environment; also his ability to interpret speech is reduced and not improved by an increase in loudness. There is no air-bone gap. There may be recruitment of loudness. Speech discrimination scores improve with increasing intensity, but do not reach normal levels.

CHAPTER 10

Thermography

The detection and display of the surface temperature of the body has found a place in medicine as an aid to diagnosis of certain disorders associated with change in superficial blood flow. Recent advances in electronics and detector design allow this detection to be done rapidly and accurately; the method is called thermography.

Thermal Imaging

The measurement of temperature at a distance from a body depends on infra-red emission. Every object with a temperature higher than absolute zero emits energy by radiation from its surface. This energy has an energy spectrum in the infra-red region of the electro-magnetic radiation spectrum. The spectrum and intensity of the radiation depend on the absolute temperature of the body and the emissivity of its surface. The relation between the total radiation from a black body (a perfect radiator) and the temperature of the body is given by the Stefan-Boltzmann equation $E = kT^4$. Skin does behave in a similar manner to a black body radiator, thus if the radiation intensity is measured it can be related directly to the surface temperature of the body.

Detectors

Two main groups of modern detectors exist for infra-red radiation: (i) thermistors—temperature-sensitive devices which change the resistance with temperature—a typical thermistor changes resistance by about 5% per degree C; (ii) photosensitive detectors, e.g. indium antimonide, these are much more sensitive detectors, especially if cooled to reduce background noise.

A Thermal Scanner

There are a number of commercial thermographic scanners available. The Barnes scanner will be described in detail (fig. 10-1). The detector is a thermistor of nickel, cobalt and

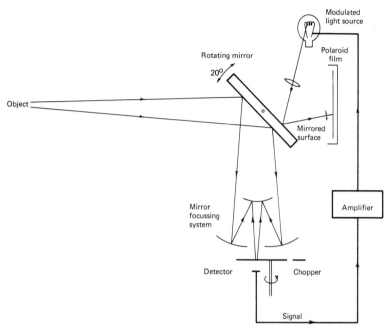

Fig. 10.1. A Barnes Scanner.

magnesium oxide in the form of a thin plate mounted on a
sapphire base; its sensitivity is 4% per degree C. It is essential in
any system of this type for the detector to have a standard of
comparison to compensate for drift in the system; this is
achieved in this scanner by chopping the signal received from
the body and interposing a black body of constant temperature
between the in-coming signal and the detector. This is done in
the Barnes instrument by using a perforated disc rotating at a
constant speed. The infra-red signal passes through the optical
system, is detected and amplified, and used to illuminate a
gas-discharge tube which glows with an intensity proportional
to the amount of radiation detected, the intensity of this light is
recorded on film. Scanning is achieved by using a mirror which
rotates on two axes. The system has an instantaneous view of
$\frac{1}{8}$ inch at 10 feet. The mirror produces a horizontal sweep of
twenty degrees; after each horizontal scan the mirror returns to
its starting point during which time the light is prevented from
reaching the film. The mirror is then tipped about a horizontal
axis by a distance equal to the width of one line. A total

vertical height equivalent to 10 degrees movement of the mirror is used, which covers about three hundred scanning lines. At 10 feet distance these angles cover a field of 28 x 40 inches. A scan may take up to several minutes depending on the temperature resolution required. The complete scan is built up on the film by making the modulated light signal follow the same scanning pattern as the detected signal; this is achieved by reflecting the light off the back of the scanning mirror. Alternative display systems may use a cathode ray oscilloscope and polaroid film (fig. 10-2).

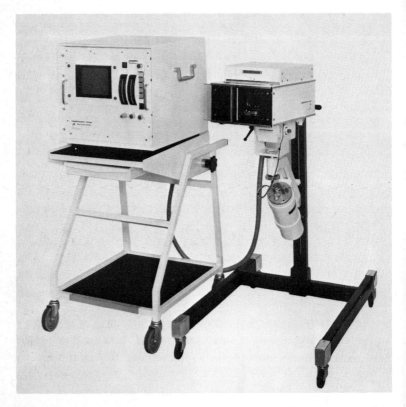

Fig. 10.2. A commercial instrument (courtesy Rank Pullin Controls).

Some Clinical Applications of Thermography

In clinical application the scanning conditions used depend on the degree of resolution required and the time to perform a scan. A scan time which is too long may allow changes in the thermal pattern to occur; a rapid scan will result in loss of temperature resolution In order to demonstrate static temperature differences a resolution of about 3 mm is desirable with temperature differences of 0.25°C, the scanning time for a full-scan would then be 2 to 3 minutes. If it is required to measure rapidly changing heat patterns in the surface of the body, scanning times of a few seconds are required. The temperature resolution should preferably be better than 0.5°C.

Diseases of the Breast

In the U.K. thermography was first developed medically to aid the diagnosis of diseases of the breast, particularly breast cancer. Since there are many factors involved that determine surface temperature in the breasts the most satisfactory method is to look for asymmetry in a thermogram of both breasts made simultaneously. The thermal pattern of normal breasts is largely symmetrical (fig. 10-3); tumours of the breast cause considerable increase in blood flow which produces dilation of the veins either in the immediate vicinity of the tumour or at a distance from it. As an initial screening test breast thermography is very valuable as it is a completely hazard-free procedure. It must be used in conjunction with special X-ray techniques if the resulting thermogram produces any doubt at all.

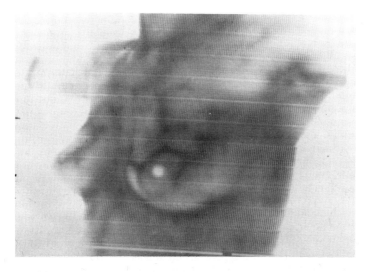

Fig. 10.3. A chest area thermogram (courtesy Rank Pullin Controls).

Dermatology

Thermography is particularly useful in determining the degree of skin damage following a burn; it can be used to estimate the viability of skin flaps after grafting operations. However, the procedure does not always produce the correct information concerning blood flow in the surface of the body as there may be contamination from chemical substances.

Peripheral Vascular Disease

The temperature of the surface of a limb determines the efficiency of its blood supply; any abrupt cold regions indicate a sudden vascular block. Thermal scanning has the advantage of visualising the vascular structure of a whole limb and can demonstrate not only the narrowing of the vessels due to disease but also the effects of drugs.

CHAPTER 11

Physiological Measurements

There is not space in this book to cover in detail the large number of subjects that come under this heading. A few subjects only will be mentioned to illustrate the application of physics in this field.

Electrical Changes in Tissues

A cell within the body tissues contains an excess of potassium ions and a deficiency of sodium and chloride ions compared with the extra cellular fluid. This difference in ion concentration produces a potential difference across the cell membrane (fig. 11-1). Any movement of one or other type of ion across

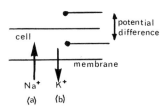

Fig. 11.1. The movement of ions during depolarisation. The concentration of K^+ at equilibrium is about 30 x that in cell compared with outside cell.

the membrane produces changes in this potential. When the system is at equilibrium there is more potassium diffusing from the cell out than in and conversely for chloride ions; a potential difference is developed across the membrane of about 60-100 mV, the interior of the cell being negative with respect to the exterior. The cell membrane is said to be polarised and the potential across the membrane is called the resting potential.

In excitable cells a stimulus brings about a transient depolarisation of the membrane usually by increasing the permeability of the membrane to sodium ions. A nerve cell is one such example of an excitable cell (see fig. 11-2). In such

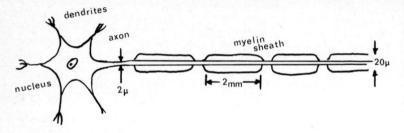

Fig. 11.2. A nerve cell showing some typical dimensions of the parts associated with conduction.

elongated cells a stimulus is propagated rapidly from the initial site of depolarisation to adjacent regions of the membrane. Once the stimulus has passed the membrane recovers its original potential. The pulse produced, which travels along the axon of the cell, is called the action potential and has the typical form shown in fig. 11-3. Notice that this is not just a depolarisation of the membrane to zero potential, but there is also a reversing of polarity so that the interior of the cell becomes positive. The transmission of the action potential occurs without significant attenuation, thus the conduction is not like that through a simple conductor; this is because the transmission is achieved by successive depolarisations. The particular mode of conduction depends on the type of nerve fibre. If the axon (2 μ diam.) is surrounded by a myelin sheath the velocity of propagation of the action potential is increased from a few metres per second to a hundred metres per second. This is because the myelin sheath consists of Schwann cells which greatly reduce the

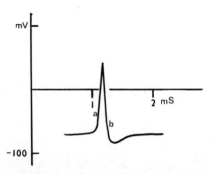

Fig. 11.3. A nerve cell action potential. a, b refer to movement of ions (see fig. 11-1).

amount of time necessary for depolarisation of those parts of the axon covered by each Schwann cell (2 mm length). When the electrical pulse reaches the end of the dendrites a chemical process is initiated which transfers the information across the synapse to the next nerve cell.

Electrical Changes Within the Heart

The heart is an incredibly compact·and efficient pump sending blood around the body by beating at a rate of seventy times per minute for 70 x 70 x 365 x 24 x 60 beats in an average life span. The heart-beat is initiated at the sinu-atrial node (the pace-maker) as a tiny pulse of electricity. This conducts through the muscle of the heart (fig. 11-4a), in a similar fashion to the conduction through nerve cells, causing the muscle to contract which forces blood from one compartment of the heart to the

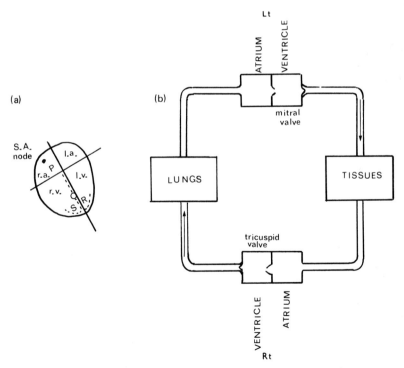

Fig. 11.4. (a) A cross-section of the heart showing the spread of the cardiac impulse from the sinu-atrial (S.A.) node through the various regions of the heart. r.a. = right atrium; l.a. = left atrium; r.v. = right ventricle; l.v. = left ventricle. (b) The heart and the circulation.

next and out into the circulation (fig. 11-4b). This heart-beat can be detected by electrodes on the heart itself or by placing electrodes at strategic points on the body surface. The latter method detects the heart-beat conducted through the body fluids and so is attenuated to an extent depending on the distance from the heart; but this method of measurement is obviously much more safe and convenient for routine purposes. During E.C.G. examination, signals are recorded from certain standardised positions on the body. The voltage signal from each lead has a characteristic shape; any divergence from this shape provides the physician with valuable information. There are different systems of positioning the electrodes. Most common at present is a ten electrode system on the torso, arms and legs. A second system uses eight electrodes, and the signals are fed into a resistive star network to produce three output signals which form an orthogonal representation of the heart-beat as a vector. A typical electrocardiogram (E.C.G.) is shown in fig. 11-5. This can be measured by amplifying the signal from the electrodes in an amplifier having a frequency response of D.C. − 100 Hz, then recording the output from the amplifier on a chart recorder. The different parts of the E.C.G. are very briefly described below:

P wave, corresponding to atrial activity;

QRS complex, results from the spread of activity to the ventricles;

T wave, represents the repolarisation (relaxation) of ventricular tissue.

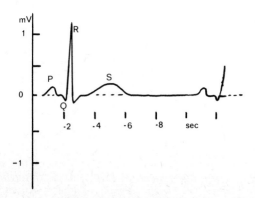

Fig. 11.5. A typical E.C.G.

Any changes in the shape or amplitude of any of these parts of the curve can help the cardiologist in his diagnosis of heart disorder.

Electromyography (E.M.G.)

The clinical measurement of the electrical activity of muscle fibre is called electromyography. The muscle action potential initiates the contraction of a muscle, it has the typical waveform shown in fig. 11-6, with a period of 6-12 ms and an

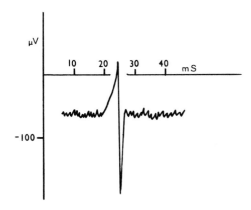

Fig. 11.6. A typical E.M.G.

amplitude of the order of 100 μV. In order to measure this a special needle electrode can be used which consists of a concentric electrode made by placing an insulated wire inside a fine gauge hypodermic needle. The central electrode must have a very fine tip of 5-10 μ. The needle itself is at the patient's earth potential. The E.M.G. signal is amplified using an amplifier with a range of frequency response 2 Hz-10 kHz and a high gain (10^6); an oscilloscope and camera are used to record the signal. A loudspeaker is also used to listen for distinctive patterns of sound associated with a particular disorder.

Electroencephalography (E.E.G.)

If electrodes are placed on the scalp of a patient the electrical activity of the brain can be recorded; generally six pairs of electrodes are used over different sites of the cortex to observe the different activities simultaneously. The signals have amplitudes of several μV and are amplified in an amplifier with a frequency response D.C. — 150 Hz. Artefact signals, which may be produced by the electrical signals of muscular activity, can be eliminated by using special techniques of differential amplification and filtration (see fig. 11-7). Various distinct patterns occur in the E.E.G. which can be identified and used to determine

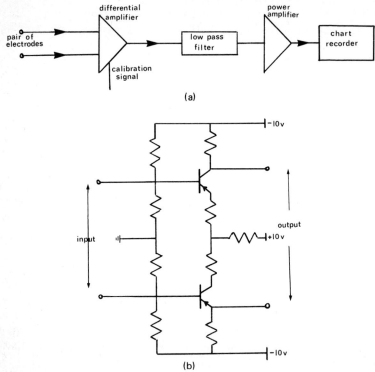

Fig. 11.7. (a) A block diagram of an E.E.G. amplifier. (b) One form of differential amplifier—all the parts can be built on a single integrated circuit chip.

normality or otherwise in the different parts of the brain. If a normal subject refrains from mental activity with his eyes closed, pulses with a frequency of 8-12 Hz arise; these are known as alpha waves. Another group of waves are the delta waves, with a frequency of 1-3.5 Hz, which appear during sleep. The presence of an intercranial tumour may cause pressure on proximal regions of the brain; these regions can become extra sources of delta activity.

Electrodes
Skin Electrodes

The most non-evasive method of recording electrical signals from the body is to use electrodes that can be easily attached to the skin surface without penetrating it. However, if the attenuation of the signal from the body is to be a minimum the contact of a skin electrode with the skin must be very good to prevent high impedance at this point. Metallic electrodes strapped to dry skin have an impedance of 100 kΩ at low frequency. To lower this resistance a gel containing a strong electrolyte is used. This penetrates the epidermis and lowers the

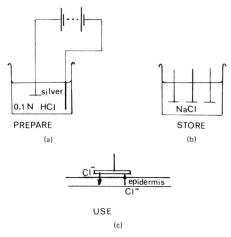

Fig. 11.8. Shows (a) the preparation, (b) storage, (c) use of a silver/silver chloride electrode.

impedance to about 1 kΩ. Polarisation at a metal-skin interface can also effectively increase the impedance. An electrode combination that has a low polarisation effect is the silver/silver chloride electrode (fig. 11-8). In this, chloride from the electrode is exchanged for chloride ions from the tissue and a balance is maintained.

Needle Electrode

To reduce the impedance at the skin-electrode interface further, small, steel, needle electrodes are used. These are inserted just under the skin as further penetration releases blood which causes fluctuations in impedance. Very fine needle electrodes are made from platinum wire, the tip of which can be only a few microns in diameter.

Pressure Changes Within the Heart

The human heart ejects about 70 cm³ of blood at every stroke, causing rapid pressure changes in the cavities of the heart. The measurement of these pressure changes can be a valuable aid to diagnosis of various heart conditions. These measurements are made during cardiac catheterisation using a combination of a long flexible catheter and a manometer and recording system. The catheter is introduced into the heart by various routes depending on the site at which it is desired to measure the pressure, e.g. by way of the antecubital vein to reach the right atrium. The parts of the heart producing the greatest pressure changes are the ventricles. A typical pressure waveform from the ventricle is shown in fig. 11-9. The various parts of this waveform correspond to the following events: (i) the sharp rise

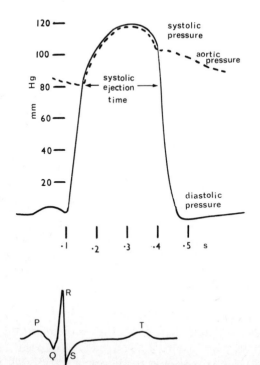

Fig. 11.9. The pressure waveform within the left ventricle.

in pressure is caused by the ventricular muscle contracting as the ventricle goes into systole; (ii) when the intraventricular pressure rises higher than the intra-aortic pressure the semi-lunar valves open and there is a rapid ejection of blood, the pressure continues to rise slowly until the end of systole; (iii) the ventricle goes into diastole and relaxes, the pressure falls sharply to almost atmospheric pressure.

Pressure Measurement

The standard method of measuring pressure within the heart relies on the catheter transmitting the pressure information accurately to the manometer (fig. 11-10). These catheters are thin flexible tubes made from materials such as polythene; the elasticity of these materials prevents them from transmitting pressure waves perfectly. The distortion of the pressure signal by the catheter depends in a complex fashion on the signal frequency. The measuring system may also have its own

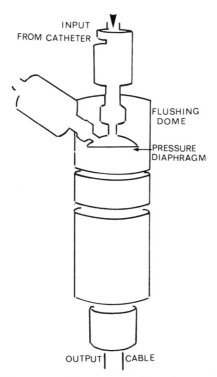

Fig. 11.10. A typical manometer head.

resonant frequency which would produce a gross increase in the pressure signal at that frequency. To allow for this the whole catheter-manometer system must be calibrated for frequency response. This should preferably be performed in two ways; (a) without the patient so that measurements can be made accurately to ensure that no gross errors are caused by the system; (b) with the patient just before pressure measurements are to be made, by running through the whole frequency range. To do the latter it is necessary to have a pressure generator that will produce pure pressure waveforms of the correct amplitude in the frequency range D.C. to 100 Hz. To provide the quick frequency response check the generator is powered from a sweep oscillating-current generator. If any outstanding change in response due to a natural frequency in the system does occur, there are various tricks to dampen the response of the system which can be used. To produce a true pressure trace the signals from the patient are recorded on magnetic tape, then processed in a computer programmed to alter the amplitude of the signal to its correct value according to the frequency response of the system.

Pressure Transducers
At the manometer end of the catheter there must be some means of detecting pressures of the order of a few hundred mmHg. Generally the pressure is made to change the shape of a diaphragm and it is this stress on the diaphragm which is detected.

The Strain Gauge
The strain gauge has more common associations with civil engineering than medicine, but small strain gauges are very sensitive to the small changes in shape of the diaphragm, especially the modern semi-conductor variety of strain gauge. The principle of the strain gauge is the change in resistance of a length of resistance wire or a strip of semi-conductor when its shape is changed. In the case of a resistance wire the resistance depends on the length (L) and cross-sectional area (A) as follows:

$$R = \rho \frac{L}{A};$$

where ρ is the resistivity. A useful measure of the sensitivity of a strain gauge is the gauge factor:

$$F = \frac{\Delta R}{R} \bigg/ \frac{\Delta L}{L};$$

i.e. the percentage change in the resistance for a proportional change in length. For example: if a nichrome wire of $R = 200\ \Omega$ and $L = 25$ mm changes resistance by $20\ \Omega$ when the length changes by 1 mm, the gauge factor, $F = 2.5$.

The wire of a resistive strain gauge is chosen to have a low temperature coefficient of resistance to avoid errors due to changes of temperature (e.g. nichrome wire has a coefficient of resistance of 4×10^{-4} ohms $\cdot$ ohm^{-1} $\cdot$ °C^{-1} at 20°C).

In the semi-conductor-type of strain gauge the gauge element is a very small strip of silicon cut from a single crystal. The gauge factors for semi-conductor strain gauges are much higher than wire strain gauges; they have typical factors of about 100. The semi-conductor strain gauge is often of the bonded type, i.e. the strip of silicon (which is a few mm in length but only 0.025 mm thick) is bonded to a base material using a resin. The change in resistance is measured on a Wheatstone bridge. To obtain maximum sensitivity all four arms of the bridge contain strain gauges (fig. 11-11). Two of these produce signals of opposite sign either: (a) by mounting resistive strain gauges on the opposite side of the diaphragm—compression causes a

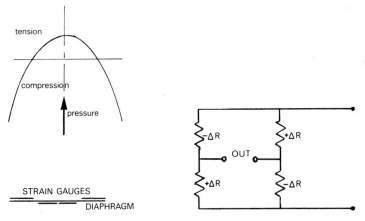

Fig. 11.11. *The change in resistance of strain gauges in a full bridge.*

decrease in resistance, or (b) in the semi-conductor type by doping with n-type impurity instead of p-type (see fig. 11-12). The signal out of a semi-conductor full bridge strain gauge is 15 mV per 300 mmHg.

Variable Inductance Transducer

A second type of transducer that is used in pressure measurements is a form of variable inductance transducer which uses the principle of the differential transformer to measure the displacement of the diaphragm. This is described with reference to fig. 11-13. The primary coil is energised with an alternating current of a frequency of about four times the signal frequency, e.g. a primary current frequency of 1 kHz is necessary for blood pressure measurements. The secondary coils are wound in opposite directions so that when the core is in the central

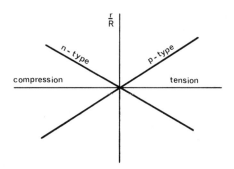

Fig. 11.12. *The percentage change in resistance for semi-conductor strain gauges of n-type and p-type.*

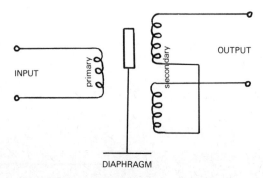

Fig. 11.13. *A variable inductance transducer.*

position, i.e. when there is no pressure signal applied, there is no net output signal. When the diaphragm is displaced it moves the core and the voltage induced in one winding exceeds the voltage in the other, producing a net output with polarity depending on the direction of movement. Within a range of movements, defined approximately by the length of the secondary coils, the voltage output is a linear function of displacement; it may have a typical value of 12 mV per exciting volt for a pressure of 300 mmHg.

The Variable Capacitance Transducer

Another basic physical parameter is the basis of design of a third type of transducer. The capacitance of two plates varies as the inverse of the distance (d) between them, i.e. $C \propto 1/d$. In the capacitance transducer one plate is kept fixed and the other moves according to the pressure applied to it. If there is a very small distance between the plates a small change in this distance will produce a large change in capacitance. The change in capacitance is measured on an audiofrequency bridge. The capacitance transducer has a high sensitivity but it suffers from the problem of poor temperature stability.

The Piezoelectric Crystal as a Pressure Transducer

The principle of the piezoelectric effect is described in the chapter on ultrasonics. A piezoelectric crystal has the characteristics of a pure transducer as a mechanical strain produces an electrical signal directly across the crystal. However, this is only useful for measuring rapidly changing pressures as a signal is only developed during a change in mechanical distortion of the crystal. It is therefore most useful for measuring high frequencies, and is used in the audiofrequency range, especially in microphones, e.g. for measuring radial artery pulses and for recording heart sounds directly from the chest wall (phonocardiography).

The Heart Sounds

A chest microphone using a piezoelectric crystal can be used to listen to the heart sounds. The interpretation of these is facilitated when used in combination with an E.C.G. recording. The common heart sounds may be summarised as follows: first sound, a low-pitched sound which coincides with the peak of the R wave and is due to the rapid closure of the atrial-ventricular valve, it lasts between 0.1-0.17 seconds; second sound, a slightly higher pitched note (about 50 Hz) due to the closure of the semi-lunar valves in the aorta and pulmonary artery at the onset of diastole (this may be split into two separate sounds if the valves do not close simultaneously); third sound, this is a very low-pitched sound due to the inrush of blood into the ventricles. Other sounds may also be recorded, e.g. a heart murmur caused by eddies produced in the blood flow by certain conditions.

MEASUREMENT OF BLOOD FLOW

This can be done electromagnetically or using ultrasound in either of the following ways: (i) measuring the transit time, (ii) using the Doppler effect.

Transit Time Method

Sound waves moving within a medium will be transported with the medium if the medium moves, i.e. the velocity of the sound waves, v, will be increased or decreased depending on the direction of movement with respect to the source. In the situation in fig. 11-14 the time taken for a pulse of ultrasound to travel from A to B is

$$\frac{L}{V + v \cos \theta}$$

and the time in the opposite direction from B to A is:

$$\frac{L}{V - v \cos \theta}.$$

The difference between these times is given by:

$$\Delta t = \frac{2Lv \cos \theta}{V^2 - v^2 \cos^2 \theta}$$

which reduces to

$$\frac{2Lv \cos \theta}{V^2} \qquad \text{for} \qquad v \ll V;$$

from which v can be calculated. For $v = 10$ cm/s and $d = 10$ cm $\Delta t \doteq 10$ nanosec, which is only possible to measure accurately by measuring the change of phase $\Delta \phi = 2\pi f \cdot \Delta t$ between the signals.

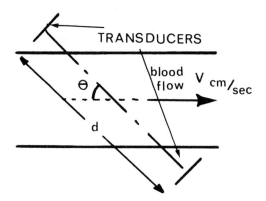

Fig. 11.14. The transit time method for measuring blood flow.

Doppler Shift Method

The most familiar occurrence of the Doppler shift effect is the change in pitch of a note noticed by a stationary observer when a car or train passes while sounding its horn. As the source of sound approaches its frequency is higher than when it is moving away. The change in frequency of the approaching source can be found as follows. In fig. 11-15 it can be seen that the

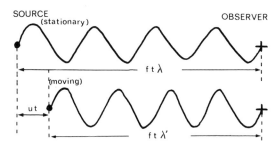

Fig. 11.15. Illustrates the change in wavelength as a source moves towards the observer.

distance between the stationary source and the stationary observer can be expressed in terms of wavelength as: $d = ft\lambda$. If the source is moving it will have moved a distance ut in a time t, but it will have emitted the same number of waves. These waves must have been compressed into a smaller space with a new wavelength defined by:

$$ft\lambda' = ft\lambda - ut \qquad (1)$$

In terms of frequency $f = c/\lambda$ and $f' = c/\lambda'$, substituting for λ and λ' in equation (1)

$$ft \cdot \frac{c}{f'} = (c - u)t \qquad \text{or} \qquad f = f'(1 - u/c) \qquad (2)$$

i.e. the observed frequency is greater than the emitted frequency by the factor fu/c.

In the Doppler shift method of determining blood flow (fig. 11-16) an ultrasonic beam is directed towards the moving blood and some energy is reflected back to the receiving crystal. The change in frequency of the reflected signal is $2fu/c$ (as it is as if the source and detector are moving apart with velocity $2u$) if the transmitted and reflected waves are moving parallel to the blood flow. In practice the transmitter and detector are at an

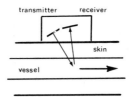

Fig. 11.16. *Transcutaneous blood flow measurement using Doppler shift.*

angle θ to the flow and the change in frequency is then $2fu \cos \theta/c$. The receiving crystal picks up the reflected signals at the original frequency as well as reflected signals at the Doppler shifted frequency and these are mixed to produce a beat wave form as the two frequencies are close in value. The beat frequency thus gives a measure of the velocity of flow. The combined signals can be demodulated to obtain the beat frequency using a system similar to that shown in fig. 11-16.

Both of these ultrasonic methods of determining blood flow are only suitable when relative values of flow are required as they only measure the average velocity. Details of the cross-section of the vessel are required to determine volume flow.

Electromagnetic Fluid Flow Measurement
A conductor moving in a magnetic field induces an electric current in a direction at right-angles to the magnetic field; this is the principle of the alternating-current generator. Blood is a

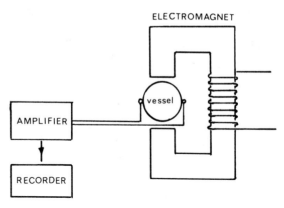

Fig. 11.17. A simplified diagram to illustrate electromagnetic blood flow measurement. The blood is moving at right angles to the page.

good conductor, so if a magnetic field is arranged as in fig. 11-17 a potential difference proportional to the average cross-sectional velocity can be detected in electrodes placed on each side of the blood vessel at right-angles to the magnetic field. The transducer head is designed to fit closely around the vessel so as to keep its diameter constant. The voltage signal is then proportional to the volume flow. The magnetic field is generated by an alternating current passing through the coils. This can be of sine- or square-wave form producing a sine- or square-wave voltage signal which can be separated from noise and artefacts before amplification.

CHAPTER 12

Recording of Physiological Signals

The Frequency Content of Signals

The simplest periodic process that occurs in Nature is described mathematically by the sine or cosine function. Such processes that perform these oscillations are said to describe simple harmonic motions. They include: the oscillation of a pendulum through small amplitudes, the vibration of a tuning fork, and pure tone sound waves. If a complete oscillation occurs f times a second the function representing the simple oscillation may be described by:

$$u = A \sin (2\pi f t);$$

where a is the amplitude and f is the frequency of the vibration. It is sometimes useful to use the concept of angular frequency: $\omega = 2\pi f$, in which case $u = A \sin \omega t$.

Pure sine-wave generators are used in audiology and in various pieces of test apparatus for pressure measuring equipment, electronic amplifiers and recorders. However, most electrical signals from the body are not of this pure wave form. A complex periodic phenomenon of the form, $F(t)$, can be represented mathematically by a Fourier series.

$$F(t) = a_0 + a_1 \cos \omega t + a_2 \cos 2\omega t + a_3 \cos 3\omega t \dots$$
$$+ b_1 \sin \omega t + b_2 \sin 2\omega t + b_3 \sin 3\omega t \dots$$

in which the choice of the constants $a_0, a_1, a_2 \dots b_1, b_2 \dots$, etc. determines the particular waveform described by $F(t)$; $f = \omega/2\pi$ corresponds to the fundamental frequency, $2f = 2\omega/2\pi$ to the 2nd harmonic, $3f = 3\omega/2\pi$ to the 3rd harmonic, $nf = n\omega/2$ to the nth harmonic, e.g. see fig. 12-2.

It is the frequency response of apparatus which is transmitting or detecting and recording the signal which determines whether a complex waveform is distorted. If there is a natural frequency of any element of the apparatus the component of the signal with this frequency will be increased in amplitude thus producing a distortion in the signal. This can occur in pressure measurement within the heart using a catheter/manometer system.

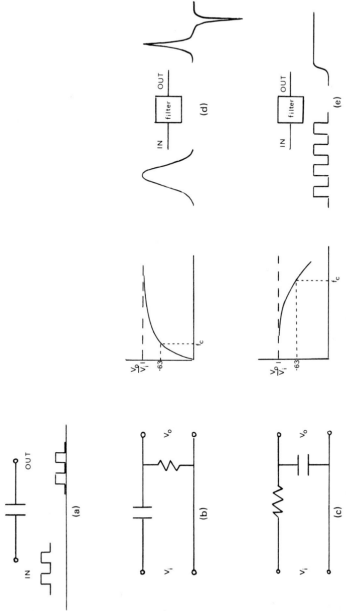

Fig. 12.1. (a) D.C. isolation; (b) High pass filter and frequency response showing the cut-off frequency $f_c = 1/2\pi RC$. (c) Low pass filter and frequency response. (d) A high pass filter as a differentiator. (e) A low pass filter as an integrator.

It is sometimes desirable to remove certain frequencies from a signal, this is done by filtration. The electrical filters for doing this are now described.

Filtration
D.C. Isolation
It is frequently necessary to remove the D.C. component from a signal, particularly if the signal comes from a high-voltage device. This is done anyway by a high-pass filter, but generally can be achieved simply by placing a capacitance of the correct rating in the signal line, fig. 12-1a.

High-Pass Filter
At low frequencies the impedance of a capacitor in this circuit, see fig. 12-1b, is such as to produce attenuation at the output because of the voltage-dividing effect. The values of resistance and capacitance are chosen to provide the required frequency response; the cut-off frequency is given by $R = 1/\omega C$. This circuit has the same characteristics as a differentiating circuit which determines the rate of change of a signal.

Low-Pass Filter
This works on the principle that the impedance of a condenser is inversely proportional to frequency, $Z \propto 1/\omega C$. High frequencies are thus passed through the condenser to earth. The resistance and capacitance are chosen to produce the desired cut-off frequency at which point the impedance of the condenser rapidly falls producing increasing attenuation of the signal (see fig. 12-1c).

Band-Pass Filter
It is sometimes desirable to pass only a range of frequencies. This can be achieved by the circuit shown in fig. 12-3, which is basically a tuned circuit in a voltage divider. Signals at the frequency to which the circuit is tuned are passed without attenuation, at other frequencies this part of the circuit becomes a high impedance so attenuating the signal.

The Combination of Signals of Similar Frequencies—The Production of Beats
The particular combination of signals of interest is when the two signals have closely similar frequencies—a few Hz apart in the

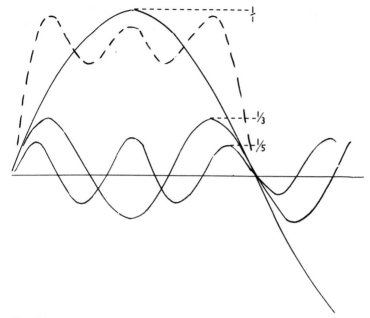

Fig. 12.2. *The representation of a square wave by its harmonic frequencies. This shows only* $Y = \sin wt + 1/3 \sin 3wt + 1/5 \sin 5\,wt.$

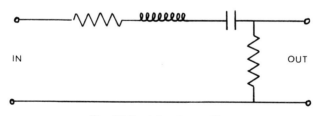

Fig. 12.3. *A band pass filter.*

audio range. An interference phenomenon results producing beats; the amplitude of the resulting signal changes at a rate equal to the difference between the signal frequencies. This can be shown by the following argument. Suppose the two frequencies are Ω_1 and Ω_2; let $\Omega_1 + \Omega_2 = 2\,\Omega$ where Ω is the mean of the two frequencies; and $\Omega_1 - \Omega_2 = 2\omega$, ω is very much less than Ω.

If the magnitudes of the two signals are the same, the sum of the signals is:

$$V \sin \Omega_1 t + V \sin \Omega_2 t$$

which can be written:

$$2V \sin \frac{\Omega_1 + \Omega_2}{2}\, t \cdot \cos \frac{\Omega_1 - \Omega_2}{2}\, t = 2V \cos \omega t \cdot \sin \Omega t,$$

i.e. an impure sine wave with amplitude varying with time—shown in fig. 12-4.

This effect is also produced when a high frequency carrier oscillator is modified (modulated) in amplitude by the signal frequency.

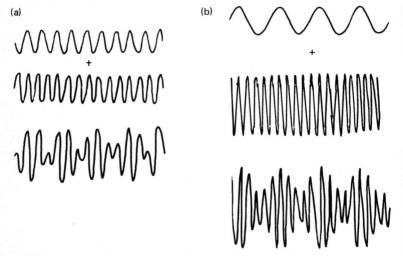

Fig. 12.4. (a) Showing how beats are formed from two signals of similar frequency. (a) A similar waveform is obtained by amplitude modulation of a carrier frequency.

To Obtain the Beat Frequency

To consider a particular example: the measurement of blood flow using an ultrasonic probe as described above. The signal received is a combination of the transmitted frequency (r.f.) and the Doppler shifted frequency. The signal is amplified in an r.f. amplifier before any processing. To eliminate signals of other frequencies, already present or introduced by the amplifier, the signal is fed through a band-pass filter, which allows a range of frequencies from $\Omega - \omega$ to $\Omega + \omega$ through. The signal is then rectified; this produces the following frequencies: D.C., ω, $2\omega \ldots$; Ω, $2\Omega \ldots$; $\Omega - \omega$, $2(\Omega - \omega) \ldots$; $\Omega + \omega$, $2(\Omega + \omega) \ldots$, etc.

A low-pass filter is used to remove the carrier frequency and its harmonics; if the cut-off frequency is correctly chosen the harmonics of ω will also be removed. This leaves ω and D.C.; a high-pass filter is used to obtain ω alone. The complete schematic circuit is shown in fig. 12-5.

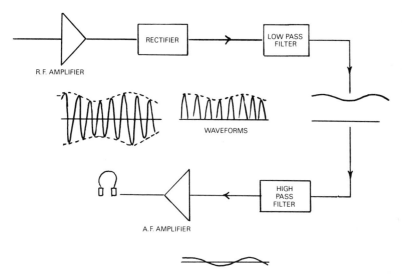

Fig. 12.5. A block diagram to show the extraction of the beat frequency.

Recording of the Output Signal

Having obtained a suitable amplitude of output signal it is necessary to record and display it so that it may be perceived and, if necessary, processed by a computer. The main considerations when choosing a recorder are: (1) the input impedance of the recorder compared to the output impedance of the signal source, (2) the frequency response of the recorder, so that if a rapidly changing signal is present the recorder shows these changes reasonably faithfully, (3) the amplitude of the signal so that it can be displayed to best advantage, (4) whether a logarithmic recording would show more information on the display.

The recording devices below have been grouped according to their frequency response.

Low-Frequency Recorders

For recording of slowly changing parameters a recorder which has a flat frequency response to only a few Hz is adequate. Chart recorders come under this heading in which the signal is used to drive a pen a distance proportional to the applied signal. This pen writes on a paper chart which moves at a definite speed in one direction. The chart is usually driven by a synchronous motor using the mains frequency; the speed is varied by various gears from, e.g. 150 mm/hr to 600 mm/min.

There are basically two types of chart recorder: (a) direct recording, (b) potentiometric recording. In the direct-recording instrument the pen is on the arm of a galvanometer (fig. 12-6)

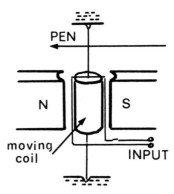

Fig. 12.6. A galvanometer movement.

and the current through the coil determines the deflection of the pen. The input signal can activate the coil directly but this requires that the source impedance is low. To overcome this difficulty an amplifier with a high impedance is used to convert the input signal, which is usually a low-current signal of the order of millivolts, to a signal with sufficient voltage and current to drive the galvanometer.

The potentiometric recorder has already been described in the section on radioisotope measuring instrumentation. It utilises a null-balancing servo-driven system which allows the input impedance to be very high, e.g. 100 kΩ. If more than one signal is to be recorded on one chart many pens are needed, each with its own potentiometer. This can make such a recorder very expensive. An alternative arrangement is to have only one potentiometer driving a multi-colour pen on a spindle which can rotate, and a switching system so that each signal is sampled for as long as it takes the pen to move into position, then the next input signal is switched in and the pen rotated; thus the recording is made sequentially.

X-Y Recorder

Instead of a moving strip of paper on which the value of y is plotted as a function of time, it is possible to put a second signal on to a potentiometer along the x-axis; this allows y to be plotted as a function of x. Thus there are two independent potentiometric circuits moving at right-angles to each other and driving one pen. This type of recorder, or plotter, is very useful for permanent record of graphic output from a computer.

Medium-Frequency Recorders

For the recording of electrical and pressure signals from the body (e.g. E.C.G.) a recorder with a flat frequency response to a value greater than 100 Hz is necessary if the signal is to be undistorted. Most of these recorders are direct writing as the response of a potentiometric system is too slow. To obtain a sufficiently fast response using a galvanometer, it is necessary to

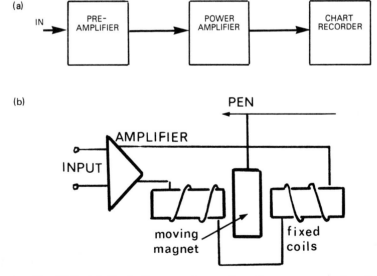

Fig. 12.7. (a) Block diagram of a medium frequency recorder. (b) Recorder movement—the pen is usually an ink jet.

reduce the inertia of the moving coil. If a small air-wound coil is used it must be used in conjunction with a more powerful magnet to have the same sensitivity as the heavy galvanometer coil. A current of the order of 100 mA is required to drive this coil. The small input signals are fed into an input amplifier which has a gain of up to several thousand; the output from this pre-amplifier is used to drive a power amplifier to provide the current necessary for the galvanometer. Alternatively the core can be a small permanent magnet, this system is shown in fig. 12-7b.

The most common method of obtaining a trace is an ink pen gravity fed through a hypodermic tube. Other methods of recording include: a hot stylus on heat-sensitive paper, a cold stylus on pressure-sensitive paper.

High-Frequency Recorders

To record signals which may have component frequencies up to several kHz, it is necessary that the recording stylus does not introduce friction by coming into contact with the chart on which the record is made. This is achieved by using a gal-vanometer-driven light probe which records a trace on photo-graphic paper. Electrostatic systems are also used in which the stylus is an electrode which deposits a charge on a special plastic chart; a charged powder sticks to the recorded line to display the trace.

Magnetic-Tape Recording

If recording only is required, in cases where the results are to be processed or can be played back later, magnetic-tape recorders can cover all the frequencies required. There are basically two approaches to tape recording depending on the fidelity re-quired: (a) direct recording, (b) frequency modulated recording. Direct recording is used for everyday purposes of recording the spoken word and music, i.e. the audio-frequency range of 50 Hz-20 kHz. In this system the output from the microphone is amplified and applied to the coil of the recording head (fig. 12-8). This head is basically an electromagnet and the magnetic tape runs over the gap in which the magnetic field is created. The magnetic flux crossing the gap magnetises the iron oxide on the tape; this flux changes with the current signal and so produces varying degrees of magnetisation in the tape. In practice a high frequency bias current is added to the signal

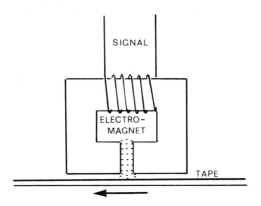

Fig. 12.8. Magnetic tape recorder head.

current to minimise distortion produced by the magnetic hysteresis in the tape.

Even with the most careful use of direct recording there are two main disadvantages: (1) that D.C. and low-frequency signals cannot be recorded, as the system only responds to changing signals, (2) it is difficult to avoid distortion of the signal, i.e. the replay signal will not correspond exactly to the input signal.

Frequency Modulation Recording

To overcome the above problems, frequency modulation of the input signal is used, i.e. the amplitude of the signal to be recorded is used to alter the frequency of a higher frequency carrier signal in a proportional manner; it is this modified high-frequency signal which is recorded. When the tape is replayed the output is demodulated to obtain a signal proportional to the input signal. The range of frequencies which can be recorded without attenuation or distortion on an f.m. system depends on the carrier frequency and the tape speed. A typical signal bandwidth (within ±1 dB) for a tape speed of 60 inch/second is D.C. − 16 kHz; as the tape speed is decreased the high-frequency end of the range falls in direct proportion to the speed.

Display Systems

Certain image display systems have already been mentioned in the sections on *in vivo* isotope tests and ultrasonic imaging.

Very often in physical and physiological measurements in medicine an immediate image is required either before or during the recording of the data.

Cathode-Ray Oscilloscope

A most widely used and versatile display system is the cathode-ray oscilloscope (fig. 12-9). The cathode-ray tube is a vacuum tube in which the direction of a beam of electrons is

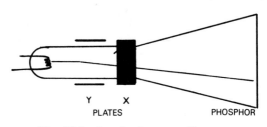

Fig. 12.9. A cathode ray oscilloscope.

controlled electrostatically and/or magnetically by horizontal and vertical deflection plates. The electrons strike the screen at the end of the tube to produce a spot image on the phosphor coating which glows with a light of characteristic colour and for a certain time (persistence) depending on the type of phosphor, some examples of which are given in the table:

Designation	Fluorescence	Phosphorescence	Persistence	Use
P1	Yellowish green	Yellowish green	24 ms	C.R.O.
P4	White	White	60 μs	T.V.
P34	Bluish green	Yellow green	100 s	C.R.O.
P33	Orange	Orange	2.2 s	C.R.O.

Fluorescence is the immediate effect of the electron interaction, phosphorescence is the after-effect which decays at a certain rate; the persistence figures given in the table are to a level of 10% of the original signal. The low persistence phosphor is used in the C.R.O. for photographic recording of medium-frequency signals; for low-frequency signals such as E.C.G. a long-persistence phosphor is used.

In many uses of the C.R.O. the deflection on the horizontal or x-axis is driven by a sawtooth waveform so that the spot on the screen is driven at constant speed from left to right, and then flys back to start the sweep again. The frequency of this waveform can be altered depending on the frequency of the signal; for low-frequency signals it is desirable to have time-base frequencies which are as low as 0.03 Hz. The signal to be displayed is applied to the vertical plates, so that $y = f(t)$ is plotted against time. In this case the brightness of the trace is kept constant.

In particular uses of the C.R.O. Where the spot is positioned by applying signals to both X- and Y-plates, e.g. in ultrasonic B-scanning or in gamma camera imaging, depending on the position of the event detected, it is usual to apply a third signal, which corresponds to the intensity of the event, to alter the intensity of the electron beam so as to produce variations in brightness on the screen. If polaroid film is used in conjunction with the correct phosphor a grey-scale image can be produced.

Storage Oscilloscope

This is an oscilloscope which has the ability to retain the image of an electrical event after the event has ceased to exist. This image retention may be extended to several hours by special methods of two-state storage systems. Only the simple storage system will be described here.

The basic elements of the oscilloscope are the same as in the conventional tube. The most important additions are shown in the fig. 12-10. The flood guns cover the whole of the collector mesh with low-energy electrons, these have not sufficient energy to pass through the potential difference at the storage mesh. When a portion of the storage mesh is hit with the high-energy electrons from the writing beam a large enough number of secondary electrons are removed from the mesh; this

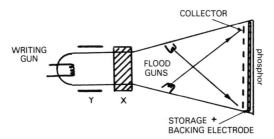

Fig. 12.10. One form of storage oscilloscope.

leaves a positively charged spot through which the flood electrons can pass to reach the phosphor and make it glow for as long as the region remains sufficiently positive. The charge is held within the insulating layer of the storage mesh. The size of the spot produced on the phosphor is larger than that on the normal C.R.O., it can be of the order of 1 mm. The range of intensity of brightness of the image is much less than the conventional C.R.O. by about 10 dB.

Television Systems

It is frequently useful to use closed-circuit television (C.C.T.V.) in medicine: to view X-ray images and infra-red images, viewing patients in radiotherapy and for demonstrations to large numbers of students. A very brief description of how a C.C.T.V. system operates and the working of the main parts will be given.

The T.V. Monitor

The principle of this is the same as the C.R.O. in that the image produced on the phosphor screen depends on a scanning electron beam. By means of deflecting coils the electron beam is deflected very rapidly and accurately in a series of lines which cover the whole screen. These lines are equally spaced and lie at a slight angle to the horizontal, see fig. 12-11. A complete set of lines is called a raster, and the region covered by the lines is called a field. At the end of the last line of a raster the electron

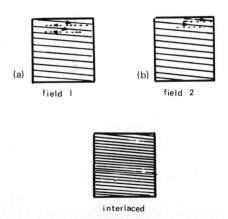

Fig. 12.11. The raster of a T.V. monitor showing the combination of two fields.

beam is deflected back to the top corner of the field. In a practical system one field is scanned with lines as in fig. 12.11(a), and a second field is scanned with its lines filling the interspaces between the lines of the first field, fig. 12-11(b). The complete picture is formed by the two interlaced fields. The picture frequency is thus half the field frequency; this provides a better image without having to increase the picture frequency. The actual picture is produced by varying the brightness level along each line. This is done by modulation of the scanning electron beam intensity at the correct place along each line corresponding to the brightness at that place on the line in the T.V. camera.

The Closed Circuit T.V. System

The deflection of the scanning beams in both camera and monitor is controlled by time-base generators; the frequency at which these operate is determined by pulses from the synchronising signal generator. The signals used for this synchronisation must be sent along the cable from the camera to the monitor along with the picture signal.

Camera Tubes

There are various types of T.V. camera depending on the purpose for which it is to be used. The simplest camera tube is the Vidicon, shown in fig. 12-12.

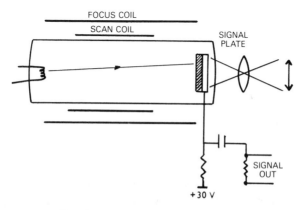

Fig. 12.12. A Vidicon T.V. camera.

Vidicon

The target is a photo-conductive semi-conductor; its electrical conductivity increases when it is illuminated with light. When an optical signal is focused on the end of the tube it will pass through the transparent signal plate and on to the target. Every bright element of the optical image will increase the conductivity at corresponding points in the target leaving on it a pattern of positive charge. When the image is scanned with the electron beam the beam produces an electrical signal in the signal plate at these points of high positive charge. As the electron beam scans the charge pattern, in the same series of lines as produced on the monitor, the magnitude of the current flowing through the resistor R will vary with the amount of charge present. It is these changes of current which, when amplified, form the picture signal.

The Image Orthicon Camera

The disadvantage of the Vidicon is its lack of sensitivity and the image lag at low-light levels. The image orthicon is a more sensitive camera tube, see fig. 12-13. The first section of the camera is similar to an image intensifier. The target is photo-emissive so that it liberates electrons when light impinges on it. These electrons are accelerated in an electric field to hit the secondary target. The charge pattern created on this target corresponds to the optical image. When the charge image is scanned with the electron beam it modulates it according to the amount of charge, but unlike the Vidicon the information is carried back in the reflected electron beam. This signal is amplified in a current amplifier, before it is fed into an external preamplifier.

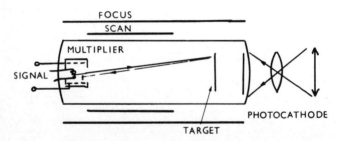

Fig. 12.13. An image orthicon camera.

Resolution and Bandwidth

The standard B.B.C. system produces 625 lines vertically on a 2-field system of $312\frac{1}{2}$ lines per field. In general 600 of these are used for the picture, this is the limiting factor on vertical resolution. In order to give the impression of movement in television it is necessary to reproduce at least 20 frames per sec. It is preferable to produce 50 frames per sec to eliminate flicker. Thus the picture repetition frequency is 25 per sec. The time for one line is then $1/(25 \times 625)$ seconds. But some of this time is used for information other than the picture itself; in general 1/5 of the time is lost, thus leaving about 50 μs for each line. To resolve a set of black and white lines the system (amplifiers, etc.) must have a bandwidth of

$$\frac{\text{no. of line pairs}}{50\ \mu\text{s}},$$

e.g. for 400 line pairs, the bandwidth must be about 8 MHz.

CHAPTER 13

The Computer

INTRODUCTION

Computers are often regarded by the uninitiated as rather frightening machines, this appears to be mainly because of a sense of some innate intelligence existing within the machine. This fear is completely unfounded; a computer can achieve nothing without instruction, and although it is possible to program it so that it can follow pathways that the programmer could not hope to follow in his lifetime it could never get out of control. Computers are also considered by some to be only the toys of scientists. Although there is some truth in the fact that scientists do spend time playing with computers, generally useful work does emerge as a result of this playtime. However, there is no doubt in any scientist's mind of the immense value of the computer as both a time and space saver. For example, the analysis of the structure of even a simple protein molecule could take a lifetime, correct use of a computer can reduce this time to a few years or even months.

It is rather strange to consider that a computer can be useful in the very human, flesh and blood environment of a hospital. But, as will be seen, it has established itself as essential in many parts of hospital work including storing of records, acquisition and processing of data, and as a routine sophisticated calculating machine. The amount of patient data is increasing rapidly and there is only a limited number of physicians to analyse it. If the computer can do the analysis, the data can be presented in a manner which allows the physician to make a quick decision and spend more time actually with his patient.

The Digital Computer

There is nothing specially magical about the computer. The basic principles are very simple: it is a device that can receive and store information; select, process and evaluate any part of this stored information, and transmit the result. The essential fact in regard to all these events is that they can take place at great speed in modern computers so that, for example, large numbers of calculations (thousands per second) can be performed in a few minutes. In modern computers the essence of good design is to fit the different functional parts of the internal organs of the computer together so that parts which work most often with each other are in close physical proximity. This is because the limiting factor on the speed of operation of a computer has become the actual time it takes for an electronic pulse to travel from one part of the computer to the next; this speed is about the velocity of light, thus it takes three nanoseconds (3×10^{-9} s) to travel along one metre of conducting wire. The actual storing and processing of data is performed by two-state systems: a switch in its on or off position, or the direction of magnetisation of a magnetic domain. The faster a system can change state the faster the processing of the stored information can take place. The earliest electrical computers contained valves for control and processing circuits; these have a switching time of the order of milliseconds. In the mid-1950's valves were replaced by transistors which can switch much more rapidly. The third generation of electrical computers was introduced in the 1960's with integrated circuits and microelectronics in general playing a large part in design; in these several complete functional circuits can be placed within a few millimetres so reducing the process time considerably.

BASIS OF OPERATION OF DIGITAL COMPUTERS

Two-State Systems

At every stage of the various functions performed by a computer: input, storage, processing, output of data, commands and signal operation, all are performed by two-state systems. This is the easiest and most economical way of dealing with the large variety of data and control systems used in computing. Many of the electrical circuits involved are very similar and it is only the conditions necessary to produce on/off states at the output that are of interest, e.g. in the simple transistor circuit shown in fig. 13-1 the voltage at the collector of the transistor is either 10 or 0 volt depending on the input voltage to the base. i.e. the transistor is off or on. Each complete two-state circuit can thus be regarded as an entity and each combination of circuits a functional device operating as a complex switch in which only the input and output binary states are of

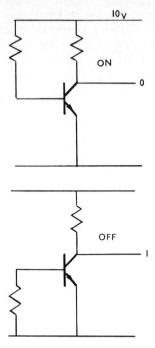

Fig. 13.1. A two-state system—the transistor as a switch.

importance. Thus detailed electrical circuitry is replaced by diagrams which represent the flow of data and show the operations performed on the data. The subject is no longer one of electricity but one of logic and the circuits perform logical operations: AND, NOT, NOR, OR, NAND, etc. There are rules for combining the operations of these circuits so that the output can be determined. These can be represented by Boolean algebra. There is not space to discuss circuits or the rules here, however, there are many books on this subject. One circuit is shown in fig. 13-2 with its associated truth table.

Binary Arithmetic

The functional elements of the computer, as described above, are based on two-state systems; the actual arithmetic operations performed must therefore be considered in terms of arithmetic to the base of two. The elements of binary manipulation of figures are described below.

The use of a decimal base in which we commonly work involves a ten-state system (0-9). The binary base system has

(a)

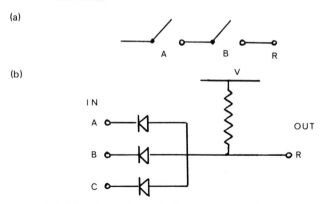

(b)

Fig. 13.2. (a) Schematic AND circuit

A	B	R
1	0	0
0	1	0
1	1	1

(b) A simple practical AND circuit

A	B	C	R
1	0	0	0
0	1	0	0
0	0	1	0
1	1	0	0
1	0	1	0
0	1	1	0
1	1	1	1

only two states, 0 and 1; thus to count beyond 1 powers of 2 are necessary in the same way as tens and hundreds, etc. are used in the decimal system. Some examples of binary numbers are given below with their decimal equivalents.

$15_{10} = 1111_2$ i.e. $1 \times 2^3 + 1 \times 2^2 + 1 \times 2 + 1$

$42_{10} = 101010_2$ i.e. $1 \times 2^5 + 0 + 1 \times 2^3 + 0 + 1 \times 2 + 0$

To obtain the binary equivalent of a decimal number it is divided successively by 2; if there is no remainder a 0 is put as the next digit, if there is a remainder a 1 is put in this position, then the resulting set of digits gives the binary number if read from the last digit, e.g.

$$
\begin{array}{ll}
2)42 & (0 \\
21 & (1 \\
10 & (0 \\
5 & (1 \\
2 & (0 \\
1 & (1 \longrightarrow 101010_2
\end{array}
$$

Addition and subtraction are the same as in any number system; they are illustrated below.

Addition

$$
\begin{array}{c}
39_{10} \\
10 \\
\underline{3} \\
52_{10}
\end{array}
\qquad = \qquad
\begin{array}{c}
100111_2 \\
1010 \\
\underline{11} \\
110100_2
\end{array}
$$

Subtraction

$$
\begin{array}{c}
39_{10} \\
\underline{10} \\
29_{10}
\end{array}
\qquad = \qquad
\begin{array}{c}
100111 \\
\underline{1010} \\
11101_2
\end{array}
$$

Anyone who has used a mechanical calculating machine will know that multiplication and division can be achieved respectively by repeated addition or subtraction with some method of shifting the numbers. However, in the computer it is quicker and more practical to use similar techniques to long multiplication and long division in binary.

Multiplication

$$
\begin{array}{c}
5_{10} \\
\underline{3} \\
\\
\\
15_{10}
\end{array}
\qquad = \qquad
\begin{array}{c}
101 \\
\underline{11} \\
101 \\
\underline{101} \\
1111_2
\end{array}
$$

Division

$$
3(21_{10}(7_{10}
\qquad
11(10101(111_2
$$

$$
\begin{array}{c}
\underline{11} \\
100 \\
\underline{11} \\
011
\end{array}
$$

Negative Numbers

It is essential that a computer is able to deal with negative numbers automatically. This is most easily done by effectively including the subtraction process in the number, so that $39_{10} - 7_{10}$ is equivalent to $39_{10} + (-7_{10})$. This is done by taking the complement of the number, i.e. its difference from zero. The complement of 7_{10}, i.e. 000111, is 111001 (n.b. all the digits of the computer word must be used); so the above sum becomes

$$100111 + 111001 = 100000 \ (32_{10})$$

A simple way of finding the complement is to change all 0's to 1's and all 1's to 0's and then adding 1 (invert and add 1).

Octal Representation

When the whole word of a 12-bit word has to be written out in full, it becomes very unwieldy and very difficult to remember or communicate, e.g. 110 011 101 001. The use of an octal base makes things much easier as each group of three binary digits is represented by a single octal digit, the above number becomes:

$$6351_8$$

Octal numbers can be manipulated before translating back to binary: e.g.

$$
\begin{array}{rcr}
6351_8 & & 3305_{10} \\
4217 & & 2191 \\
\hline
12570_8 & = & 5496_{10}
\end{array}
$$

making programming much easier.

Input Devices

To get data and program into the computer some form of input device must be used that reads binary numbers and puts them into the computer store (see fig. 13-3). The preparation of a program is usually done by punching paper tape or cards with binary codes in which holes represent the state 1. Special typewriters have punching systems attached to them that punch the correct code on the tape or card when the character is struck on the keyboard. Each character has its own binary code. A standard code system for paper tape is ASCII (American Standard Code for Information Interchange) which uses an 8-bit array taking up a width of one inch of paper tape. Ten characters occupy one inch of length of tape, thus to store a two hundred page novel on paper tape would need about 5,000 feet. The standard teletype reader can transform each character on the tape into a binary electrical signal which is passed into the computer at the rate of ten characters per second. This is a

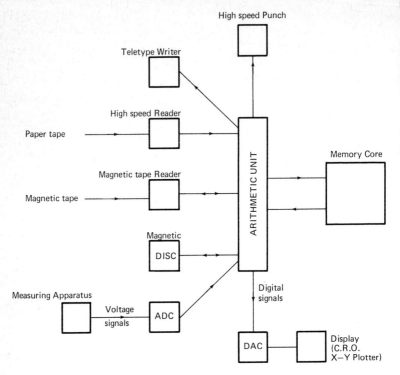

Fig. 13.3. Block diagram showing the relationship of some input/ output devices to the computer.

relatively slow rate because this type of reader is an electro-mechanical device. Fast readers of tape operate on a photocell system to detect the holes and can read at a rate of 300 characters per second.

A card reader detects the punched holes in cards with twelve rows and 80 columns; a mechanical reader can operate at the rate of 100-300 cards per minute whereas a photoelectric reader can operate at 1,000 cards per minute. Information on paper tape or cards is usually of the actual program which has been prepared at a teletype independently of the computer. With a small computer, or at a terminal to a large computer, it is possible to communicate directly with the computer using the teletype. This is especially useful when formulating a program in a high-level language, as corrections to the program can be made immediately using some form of editing.

The Computer Store

The main types of computer store may be divided into three sections depending on the speed with which information may be written into or read out of the store; the time this operation takes is designated the access time.

Immediate Access Store

The access time of this type of store is of the order of a few microseconds. Core store is the only type of store that can come into this category. It is formed from two-state elements that can be rapidly and directly accessed even when the complete core may consist of an array of 64 x 64 elements. The most common type of core store at present available consists of arrays of ferrite toroids. Several wires pass through each toroid to control the polarity of the magnetisation and to sense this polarity (see fig. 13-4).

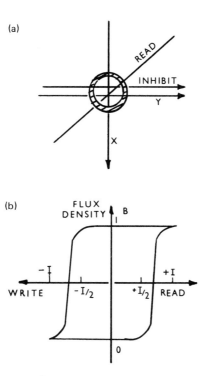

Fig. 13.4. (a) A ferrite toroid with its read-write wires. (b) The square hysterisis loop of a ferrite core.

Each core is an element of a matrix which can be located in Cartesian co-ordinates. To change the state of a core element a "write" current is sent along the desired X and Y wires, and only where these wires meet is the combined current of sufficient magnitude to change the state of that element. To sense the state of an element ("read") the same system of selection is used, but the current is of opposite magnitude to the "write" current. If the selected core element contains a 0, this read pulse does not change its state. However, if the core contains a 1, the read pulse changes the core's state from 1 to 0. This change in magnetic flux induces a voltage in a read wire which carries the information of the state of the core element to the output. The read currents necessarily destroy the original

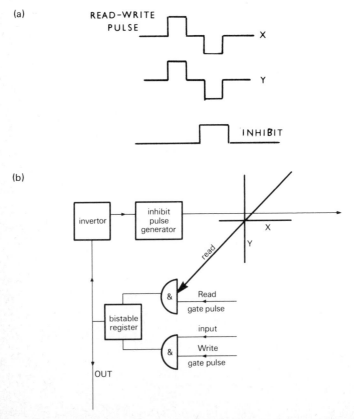

Fig. 13.5. (a) Read-write and inhibit pulses. (b) Schematic read-write circuits of ferrite core. (After Harvey.)

information on core elements containing 1; thus a "write" pulse must immediately follow the read pulse to restore the original state. However, this "write" pulse would change elements originally containing 0, so in this case the "write" pulse is cancelled by an inhibit pulse. This complicated series of events is most conveniently illustrated in diagrammatical form (fig. 13-5).

Rapid Access Store

This consists of a magnetic drum or disc which can contain 4-100 thousand words of store. It acts as an intermediate store to hold programs and data for rapid placing into core store when necessary.

The Magnetic Drum. As with all magnetic recording systems the storage of binary digits is achieved by changing the magnetic state of a minute part of a magnetic oxide coating (a magnetic domain). The metal drum on which this coat is placed is typically about 20 cm diameter and 30 cm in length (fig. 13-6)

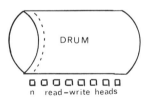

DRUM

n read—write heads

Fig. 13.6. Magnetic drum.

and rotates at 2,000-6,000 r.p.m. There are two systems for obtaining and storing information from a magnetic drum: (i) serial—each read-write head reads from its own track one complete word, e.g. each track may contain thirty-two words and there may be 256 tracks in which case the total number of words which can be stored is 256 x 32. (ii) Parallel—for an n-bit word there are n read-write heads so that all the bits of a complete word can be read simultaneously. The access time for a magnetic drum depends on where the required word is on the drum in relation to the distance from the read head at that instant. A typical mean access time is about ten milliseconds.

The Magnetic Disc. A flat disc of metal coated with a layer of magnetic oxide can store more bits of information than a drum.

Many discs can be stored on top of each other, each with its own read head which moves radially to choose the track on which the required word is written. Access time is slower than a drum, but still less than one second.

Slow Access Store
   Magnetic Tape. Very large quantities of information may be stored on magnetic tape as there are several hundred feet of tape on each reel. This type of store forms the main part of the permanent store in large computers for data and programs. Access times vary from several seconds to several minutes depending on the position of the required data on the tape.
   Paper Tape and Punched Cards. These are the forms of store for the user's permanent record of programs or data. The reading times are so slow that in large computers programs on paper tape or cards are always transferred directly to magnetic tape before any processing by the computer is performed.

Output
For large computers operating batch processing for large numbers of users, rapid output of large volumes of information from possibly several hundred different programs a day is needed. In this case a line printer is essential. These can operate at between 150 and 1,000 lines of print per minute. They work on the principle of having all the necessary characters on wheels with one wheel for each character space of line. The correct character at each position along the line is spun into position, and when all the characters for a given line are in place the whole arm holding the wheels comes forward to strike the paper.
   For an individual operating a terminal to a large computer or directly operating a small computer, a teletypewriter operating at 10-30 characters per second is adequate for outputting answers. When editing a program from a terminal a storage scope display with a keyboard is preferable as it can write at a greater speed. Other forms of output are required as follows: (i) punched paper tape output; this can be obtained from a teletype or high-speed punch; (ii) graphical output; there are two methods of obtaining this (a) directly from the binary numbers on to an incremental plotter which may have 4,096 points along both X and Y directions of a Cartesian co-ordinates system, (b) by converting these digits to an analogue signal to

drive an X-Y plotter, this is less accurate than an incremental plotter as it is subject to zero drift and calibration errors; (iii) graphic output on to oscilloscope or storage oscilloscope from a digital to analogue converter.

Digital to Analogue Converter (D.A.C.)
In cases where a voltage signal is required to output data from the computer the binary code must be converted into a voltage. A simplified circuit to do this is shown in fig. 13-7. The switches are operated if the particular binary digit contains a 1 at that position; a voltage is developed at the output which is a definite fraction of the supply voltage to the circuit.

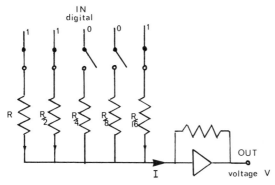

Fig. 13.7. A schematic diagram of a digital to analogue converter. If a 1 is produced by a voltage V, the current I is given by: $I = V + 2V + 16V$ i.e. $I \alpha 19$. Reading from the right the digit is 19_{10}.

Analogue to Digital Converter (A.D.C.)
The opposite device to a D.A.C. is the A.D.C. which really forms an input device to a digital computer. In situations where experimental data from a piece of apparatus is in the form of voltages, these are either stored on magnetic tape or fed directly into the computer (on line) so that they can be processed. Before this is possible on a digital computer it is necessary to change the analogue signal into a digit suitable for the computer. One method of doing this is shown in fig. 13-8. Pulses from a clock-pulse generator (10 kHz) are counted for a time interval determined by the voltage; this count is then proportional to the

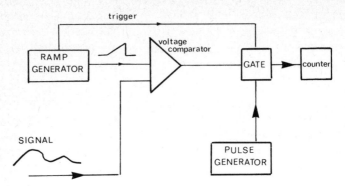

Fig. 13.8. A block diagram of one form of analogue to digital converter.

instantaneous voltage at the input. The gate to allow the pulses through is opened by a trigger which operates at the start of the ramp and is closed by a signal from the voltage comparator when the ramp voltage equals the input voltage. A counter accepts the number of clock pulses allowed through the gate during this time.

USE OF THE DIGITAL COMPUTER

There are two broad categories of computer: large and small. The large computer has a large core store, many millions of words of backing store, and all the peripheral equipment, which needs a permanent staff to operate it. The user cannot actually run the computer himself. He is allocated a code number so that he can enter programs into the computer and run them, but can only use a definite amount of computer time a week. He prepares his programs off-line and then presents a stack of punched cards to the operators of the computer. These are fed into the backing store and then either batch processed at a conveniently quiet time or held in a backing store until the user operates a terminal and calls his program for editing or running. At this point if there are other users operating their programs simultaneously the computer sorts out the timings of the various programs and brings them from the backing store into the intermediate access store for rapid placing into core store. This type of large computer is frequently operated from terminals at a distance from the computer by transfer of information along the public telephone lines. The binary pulses produced by a teletype must be converted to audiofrequency signals by means of a modulator and the signals passed from the computer must be converted back by a demodulator. The modulator-demodulator units are known as *modems.*

The small computer is usually operated directly by the user who will then monopolise the computer and all its peripherals. He will call his program from magnetic tape or disc store into core store and then run or edit it, interacting directly with the computer. Small computers are now frequently coupled directly to complicated apparatus so that experimental data can be processed directly.

Principles of Operation (fig. 13-9)
The Control Unit

An essential part of any computer is the mass of electronic circuits that control the movement of binary words from input devices into memory, out into the arithmetic units, back into

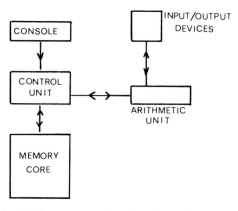

Fig. 13.9. A block diagram showing the relationship between the various units of the computer.

memory, and out on to output devices at completion. Each computer is designed so that its circuits respond to a particular set of binary codes. This set of codes is designed in conjunction with the circuits so as to work at maximum efficiency.

Programming

Before any program can be fed in automatically under computer control, certain instructions in a special code must be toggled-in manually. A binary loader in this special code can then be fed in; and then any program in binary code can be loaded. To write programs in binary is very tedious, thus language compilers are developed to translate simple strings of characters (mnemonics) into binary codes. The compiler of the particular language required is placed into core store, the user's program is placed in an input device and fed in automatically under computer control using instructions from the compiler. The compiler then produces a binary tape of the program which can be fed in using the binary loader. This sequence is illustrated in fig. 13-10.

The binary program consists of a sequence of binary-coded instructions with each instruction allocated to a definite address in the core store. When the binary program has been loaded into the core it can be started at the first address and will then automatically follow the required sequence of instructions.

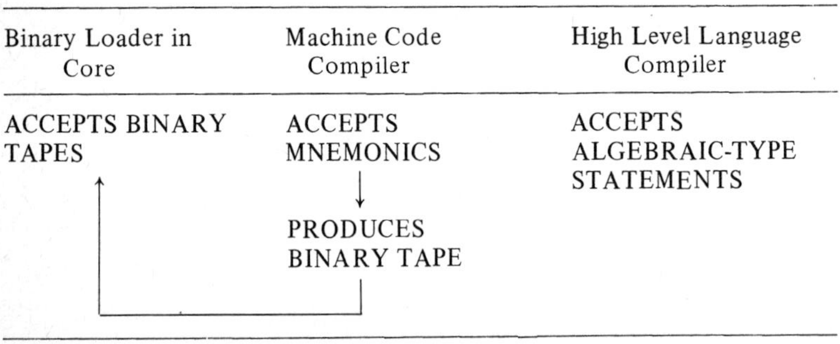

Binary Loader in Core	Machine Code Compiler	High Level Language Compiler
ACCEPTS BINARY TAPES	ACCEPTS MNEMONICS	ACCEPTS ALGEBRAIC-TYPE STATEMENTS
	PRODUCES BINARY TAPE	

Fig. 13.10. Different levels of programming.

Addressing

Each binary code is made up of several parts. In the simplest system each code contains a function (i.e. a command) and an address related to the function. For example, in the machine code used by Digital[1] computers there are seven basic commands (see table) which take up the first three characters of the 12-bit word, the other characters are used for the address. If the core store exists in sections of 4,096 bits a 12-bit word is not sufficient to contain a command and to address directly all the

[1] Digital Equipment Corporation.

Table 13.1

Machine Codes

AND	000	Performs an AND operation with contents of address and contents of accumulator
TAD	001	Adds the contents of the address into the accumulator
ISZ	002	Adds one to the contents of the accumulator, if this now equals zero miss the next command
DCA	003	Deposits contents of accumulator in specified address, clears accumulator (sets all digits to zero)
JMS	004	Jump to subroutine specified by address; after performing subroutine return to do next command
JMP	005	Jump to address specified and continue performing commands in sequence from there.

A 12-digit word may consist of:

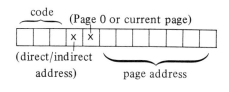

e.g. TAD B =

$$\boxed{0\,|\,0\,|\,1\,|\,0\,|\,0\,|\,0\,|\,0\,|\,0\,|\,1\,|\,0\,|\,0\,|\,0}$$

1   0   1 0_8

(see below)

A Simple Program in Machine Code

0200	START,	CLA	(Address 200 given the name START; clear accumulator)
0201		TAD A	(Add the contents of address A into accumulator)
0202		TAD B	(Add the contents of address B into accumulator)
0203		AND C	(Perform AND between A + B and C)
0204		ISZ	(Adds one to accumulator)
0205		JMS NEXT	(If accumulator is not zero jump to subroutine NEXT)
0206		HLT	(If accumulator is zero, halt the programme)
0207	A,	3331	
0210	B,	4331	
0211	C,	0115	
0300	NEXT		

Table—*continued*

Binary Code Prog.

ADDRESS	CODE
0200	7200
0201	1007
0202	1010
0203	0011
0204	2000
0205	5100
0206	7402
0207	3331
0210	4331
0211	0115

core bits. Thus indirect addressing must be used in which the address following a command contains the actual address to be used. Indirect addressing is achieved by changing the fourth bit of a word to a 1.

Machine Language Assembler

A program written in machine language contains the command codes, numbers, names, and addresses which can be given names for easy reference when using subroutines. The assembler will convert these codes into binary and the names into the correct address positions and place everything in the correct order (see simple program).

High-Level Languages

Machine code programs use the particular computer for which they are designed in the most efficient way; however, they are difficult programs to write and are used only by expert programmers. High-level languages are designed so that they can be learnt and used easily; they are often algebraic in nature so that mathematical expressions can be written with ease. Fortran is one such language for general purposes used by many machines and can deal with many kinds of problems both algebraic and symbolic. Focal is used by Digital computers and is very simple to learn. An example of a Focal program is given below:

To calculate the expression $y = \log (x^4/x^2 - x)$ for values of x requested by the operator:

    1·1   ASK X

    1·2   SET Y = FLOG{(X ↑ 4)/[(X*X) − X]}

    1·3   TYPE Y; GO 1·1

USES OF THE DIGITAL COMPUTER IN MEDICINE

E.C.G. Analysis

Electrocardiograms present a large amount of information to the cardiologist which he uses to help him with his diagnosis based on years of experience. It is possible for a computer to deal with this type of information either by recording the E.C.G. signals and then feeding them into the computer at a later time, or by linking the computer directly to the E.C.G. machine. The E.C.G. is in analogue form and must be converted to proportional digits by an analogue to digital converter, which can be adjusted to sample the wave form at any desired rate per second. The computer program to process E.C.G. data is complex as it is necessary to provide the computer with criteria for recognising the various parts of the E.C.G. Once the different waves have been identified their amplitudes are measured and the time intervals between various parts of the complete PQRST wave may be measured. These are averaged over a large number of heart-beats and the data displayed and typed out for the clinician to use in his diagnosis. At present this processing takes up to $\frac{1}{4}$ hour for each complete recording. Less detailed analysis is used in intensive care units using a small "computer" on-line to monitor the E.C.G.s of the patients in the unit and to determine when the heart rate rises above a pre-set level in any of the patients; at which point an alarm sounds to alert the nursing staff.

Pressure Measurement Analysis

A large amount of information concerning heart function is available from pressure measurements made within the heart during catheterisation of the heart. The pressures are obtained by means of catheter/manometer systems which have a frequency response not necessarily flat or reproducible. If the pressure data is recorded it can at a later stage be analysed by the computer in the same way as E.C.G. signals, and at the same time can be corrected for the frequency response of the system.

Isotope Test Calculations

The calculations involved in some radioisotope tests, although simple in principle, may be complicated mathematically as decay factors, background counts, etc. are needed, and mistakes can easily be made. It is relatively simple to write short programs in a high-level language to perform these calculations (e.g. see program below). This provides a certainty and speed of calculation. It also allows for a further degree of automation; the automatic sample counter of *in vitro* samples can be provided with a paper tape punch so that each count and counting time for every sample is punched on paper tape. This data can then be fed directly into the computer so that the result of a test can be obtained quickly.

A Simple Isotope Test Calculation in Focal

To calculate iodine uptake:

```
Prog.        Comment
ASK ST       (ST = standard count)
ASK T        (T = time between measuring standard and performing measure-
                  ment on the patient)
SET S = ST*[FEXP(– LT)]    (L = decay constant)
ASK BK       (BK = background count);
        SET S = S – BK (subtract background)
ASK PT       (PT = Patient count)
ASK BB       (BB = Blood background)
SET P = ((PT – BB)/S)* 100; TYPE "% UPTAKE =", P, "%".
```

Computer Smoothing of Curves

The information from rate meters on apparatus used for renograms or cerebral transit time is degraded by the rate meter and recording system since there are two processes of conversion from the original information to the final record: (i) digital to analogue, (ii) analogue to analogue; and analogue systems are subject to zero drift and calibration errors. If direct digital recording of counts into cells of equal time length is made the information is more accurate, but there are still Poisson counting errors. If the counts are recorded on punched paper tape these fluctuations can be reduced by some form of fitting using the counts on either side of a particular point to obtain a closer value of the real count at that point. A common

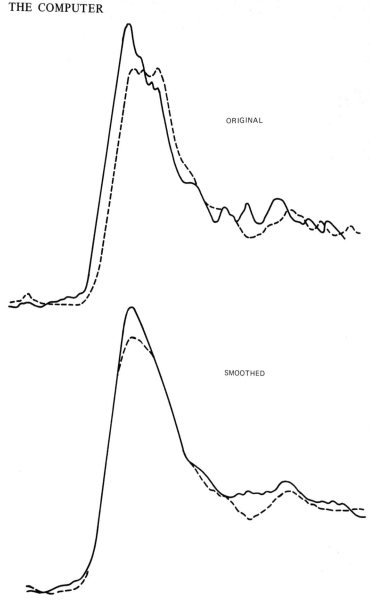

ORIGINAL

SMOOTHED

Fig. 13.11. The effect of smoothing on cerebral transit time curves.

technique is to use a polynomial of a second order fitted by least squares. An example of curve smoothing is given in fig. 13-11.

Data Processing in Scanning

The normal scan produced by a colour dot or photo dot system is pictorially useful without any further processing if the defect to be detected is fairly prominent. However, if there is any uncertainty of diagnosis, computer processing of the data can be very valuable. The data is recorded' in a form suitable for processing by the computer on magnetic tape. One method of achieving this, if the horizontal movement of the scanner is driven by a stepping motor, is to arrange for the scintillation pulses to be recorded on a scalar for a time equal to an integer number of pulses of the stepping motor; this ensures that the counts are contained in equal cells of the line scan and changes in velocity of the scanning head do not affect the result. The computer can be used to process the data in various ways, but essentially the aim is to smooth out the rapid fluctuations due to statistical variations (which can be sufficient to change the colour on a colour dot system) so that any real changes of isotope distribution can be seen; however, the smoothing must not be done to such an extent that real information is lost. Smoothing can be done relatively simply by using the information on either side of a particular value and position of a scan line to obtain a closer value to the real intensity level at that point; this is a "best fit" method of analysis. Alternatively smoothing may be achieved by some form of filtration of the signal to remove unwanted frequencies; this can be done electronically using low-pass or band-pass filters. The final isotope distribution from the computer can be displayed in a number of ways: (1) the information is fed back into the original display system, e.g. colour dot; (2) if the computer has a line printer this can be used with a character for each intensity level; (3) iso-activity contours may be plotted on an incremental plotter.

Computer Diagnosis

There is a fear among some that computers could take over control of everything if allowed to do so, thus inevitably there is considerable opposition to the idea of a computer asking questions of a patient, then producing a diagnosis and a packet of pills. However, as long as the concept of computer diagnosis is not taken too far there are signs that, working hand-in-hand with the physicians, the computer can produce very reliable differential diagnosis of well-defined disorders. The basis of the system is that the computer is used as a decision-making machine following specific pathways with the direction taken at each junction (fig. 13-12) decided by a probability function. The data from clinical studies of previously encountered patients are used as the elements for calculating this probability function. To improve the accuracy of the system at certain points it is desirable to have as many parameters as possible determined using objective tests performed on the patient, e.g. thyroid uptake, vitamin B_{12} absorption. The values of these tests can be compared directly with known ranges of values attributed to

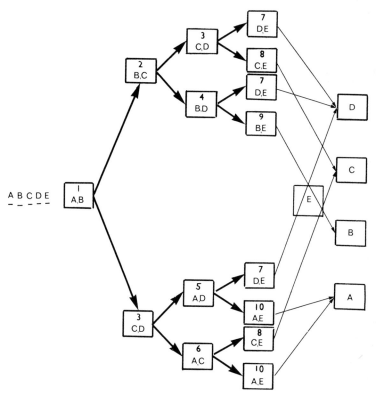

Fig. 13.12. A block diagram showing how a patient suffering from one of a group of possible 5 diseases (A. B. C. D. E.) can be tested to eliminate all but one. In practice 10 tests would not be necessary as each test could produce a probability factor for each disease, which the computer could use to determine more quickly the most likely disease.

certain disorders, this is much more valuable than the vague subjective statements of the patient. In diagnostic problems requiring the differential diagnosis of up to ten possibilities the computer will be very valuable as a diagnostic aid.

Radiotherapy Treatment Planning

The detailed production of a combined isodose distribution in radiotherapy is a skilled but tedious task. Performing this quickly and accurately on a computer would relieve personnel to allow them to concentrate on other aspects of treatment planning; it would also allow for a number of plans to be produced quickly for the same patient so that the best can be chosen. Alternatively the computer can be programmed to perform optimisation procedures to produce the best plan for given conditions.

There have evolved two distinct systems for achieving the same end in computer treatment planning. The basic data can be in the form of the original isodose charts tabulated in a suitable form for the computer, and stored on magnetic tape. The planning programme consists of a series of questions to the user concerning the position of the various radiation beams (fields), their dimensions, etc., followed by a series of instructions to combine the values of the dose contribution from each field on a matrix of points. The contour levels corresponding to the requested values of dose are then plotted automatically on a storage oscilloscope. If the result is not satisfactory various field parameters can be changed and the contour level for this new arrangement can be plotted. When the best plan has been found it is plotted on an incremental plotter to obtain a permanent record of the dose distribution to be kept in the patient's notes.

An alternative system is to calculate the dose at every point on a matrix from empirical formulae. This requires only a few parameters for each radiotherapy machine and thus does not need mass storage. The whole programme need only occupy 8,000 words of store and allows for more variety in field size, field modification, etc. than the mass storage system. Its main disadvantage is the time needed to perform each calculation.

Whichever system is used the best use of it will be made if it is in close proximity to the other devices used in treatment planning, e.g. simulator, body contour devices, etc. In this way the computer can be used interactively with the patient on the

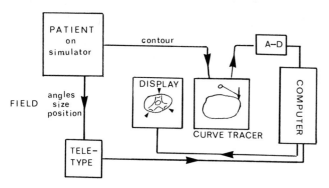

Fig. 13.13. A block diagram showing the computer and some of the peripheral devices used in treatment planning.

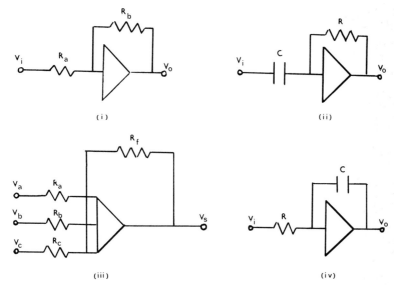

Fig. 13.14. Some electrical analogues.

(i) multiplication by a constant $V_0 = V_i . (R_b/R_a)$.

(ii) Differentiation $V_0 = \dfrac{dV_i}{dt} \cdot (R\,C)$

(iii) Summation $V_s = V_a \cdot \dfrac{R_f}{R_a} + V_b \cdot \dfrac{R_f}{R_b} + V_c \cdot \dfrac{R_f}{R_c}$.

(iv) Integration $V_0 = \dfrac{1}{R\,C} \displaystyle\int V_i$.

simulator, so that any alteration made to the fields to improve the dose distribution can be immediately checked on the simulator. A complete treatment planning suite is shown in fig. 13-13.

ANALOGUE COMPUTING

In the digital computer all parameters are represented by numbers; instead of this a parameter can be represented by another parameter proportional to it. This forms the basis of an

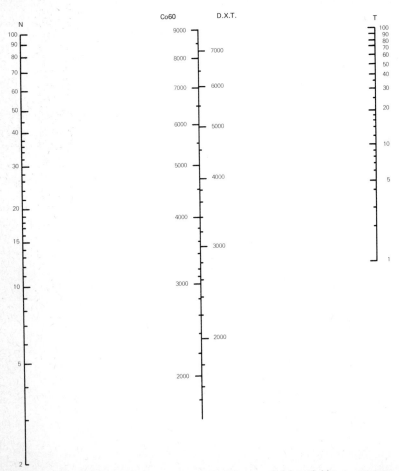

Fig. 13.15. A nomogram to solve $D = N.S.D./(N^{0.24} \cdot T^{0.11})$ for N.S.D. = 1800 rets. for either higher energy radiation (cobalt-60) or medium energy radiation (250 kV X-rays).

analogue computer. For example, the flow of blood through the body can be represented by the flow of electricity through a complex arrangement of electrical devices that alter the flow. The great advantage of the analogue is that any parameter in the system can easily be altered and the flow at any point can be measured. However, the electrical analogue can only represent a model of the system which may not necessarily be perfect. Some simple examples of electrical analogues are shown in fig. 13-14. It is also possible to generate more complex mathematical functions such as exponential, sine, etc. There are also mechanical analogue computers, the commonest of which is the slide rule, which can be used to solve various forms of equation, the parameters for which are engraved on the rule. Nomograms are also a form of analogue computer and can be very useful for routine calculations. The nomogram in fig. 13-15 can be used to solve the equation $NSD = D \cdot N^{0.24} \cdot T^{0.11}$ which approximately represents the biological effect of fractionation in radiotherapy.

Optical image processing is a form of analogue computing. Optical filtering is performed on the diffraction pattern of the original image. Highly coherent light from a laser is used.

Glossary

IONISING RADIATION

Absorbed dose: energy per unit mass imparted by ionising radiation to a small mass. Special unit: 1 rad = 10^{-5} J/gm.

Absorption spectrum: the spectrum of intensity (measured by count rate for ionising radiation) against energy detected by a radiation detector.

Afterloading: an internal radiation technique which reduces the radiation hazard to the operator by a system which allows the active sources to be placed in receptor tubes after these tubes have been correctly positioned.

Biological half time: the time needed to remove half the amount of a compound from the body.

Bolus: designates a volume of injected tracer which travels in the body without substantial dispersion during a test.

Bremsstrahlung: the continuous X-ray spectrum produced when electrons are slowed down by collision with nuclei.

Characteristic radiation: photons emitted when an atom in an excited state, due to the removal of an electron from a specific orbit, returns to its ground state. The photon energy is determined by the electron energy level and is therefore characteristic of the atom.

Collimation: the use of heavy metal absorbers to define the dimensions and direction of a radiation beam.

Compton edge: the maximum energy given to the recoil electron from photon scattered through 180°.

Cyclotron: an accelerator which uses an oscillating magnetic field to accelerate high energy photons by induction to produce neutrons for (n, γ) reactions.

Einstein's equation: relates energy, E, released or destroyed in nuclear reactions to the mass, m, of created or destroyed particles: $E = mc^2$.

Emission spectrum: the spectrum of intensity against energy emitted from a radiation source.

Exposure (dose): this is a measure of radiation dose in terms of ionisation in air. Defined at $\Delta Q / \Delta m$ where ΔQ is the sum of the electrical charges on all the ions of one sign produced in air when all the electrons liberated by photons in a volume element of air whose mass is Δm, are completely stopped in air.

Fission product: artificial radioactive nuclide produced in fission reaction.

Focal spot size: the apparent area of an X-ray source on an X-ray target.

Free radicals: transient, highly reactive, chemical combinations.

Ground state: the lowest energy state for a given nuclide.

Half-value thickness: the thickness of a medium required to reduce the intensity of a narrow beam of radiation to half its initial value.

Ionisation: the removal of an electron from an atomic orbit.

Isomeric states: states of a nucleus having different energies and half-lives.

Isotopes: nuclides having the same atomic number.

Lead equivalence: the amount of lead needed to reduce radiation by the same factor as the protective material used.

Lead glass: glass with a high lead content for protection purposes.

Lead rubber: rubber sheet containing a uniformly distributed lead salt.

Leakage radiation: radiation which escapes from the protective housing of a source.

Magnetron: an electronic valve which produces high power radio frequency waves.

Metastable state: isomeric states with energies above the ground state.

Nuclide: a specific nucleus determined by its mass number.

Radiation energies: low-energy X-radiation—up to 140 kV exciting potential; medium-energy X-radiation—150-300 kV exciting potential; high-energy X-radiation—over 1 MV effective potential.

Radiation particles: alpha—the nucleus of a helium atom; beta—nuclear electrons; electron—high energy electrons for treatment produced by accelerator or betatron; gamma—photons produced from excited nuclei, identical to X-ray photons; neutron—neutral nucleon of atom; proton—positively charged nucleon of atom, can be accelerated in cyclotron to high energy.

Relative biological effect: the effect of a given radiation on a biological entity compared to the effect produced by the same dose of a second form of radiation.

Scale of two: the basic counting circuit of a scaler—produces one output pulse for two input pulses.

Scalloping: the effect produced in bi-directional scanning due to a delay in the display of count rate (produces a zig-zag pattern of a line source).

Specific activity: strictly mCi/mg of an element, but more commonly mCi/g of a compound of which the element is a part.

Waveguide: a rectangular or cylindrical metal tube which is needed to conduct high frequency electromagnetic waves.

ULTRASOUND

Absorption coefficient: the reduction in intensity of an ultrasound beam usually expressed in dB/cm.

Bandwidth: the range of frequency in which the performance of a device, e.g. amplifier, is constant.

Cavitation: the development of cavities within a liquid when the pressure within the liquid exceeds atmospheric pressure at the surface of the liquid.

Curie point: the temperature at which piezoelectric characteristics are lost.

Degrees of freedom: the number of alternative movements of a body.

Free radicals: highly reactive atoms or molecules with too few or too many electrons.

Huygens' principle: any wave phenomenon can be analysed by the addition of contributions from some distribution of simple sources in phase and amplitude to represent the physical situation.

Menières disease: a progressive degeneration of the structures of the inner ear.

Natural frequency: the frequency at which a body will oscillate following a transient impulse.

Polarisation: an alignment of charge.

P.R.F.: pulse repetition frequency.

Schlieren (photography): light passing through a transparent medium is refracted wherever the density of the medium varies; the phenomenon is known by the German name schlieren. Schlieren photography uses special optical systems to study sound and ultrasound waves in gases and liquids.

PHYSIOLOGICAL MEASUREMENTS

Action potential: the change in potential difference across a cell membrane during depolarisation.

Amplitude modulated: (AM) the amplitude of a carrier frequency is modified by the input signal.

Angular frequency: $\omega = 2\pi f$, where f is the signal frequency.

Audio-frequency bridge: an A.C. bridge operated at audio frequency.

Bandwidth: the range of frequencies over which the frequency response of a device is constant.

Beat frequency: the combination of signals of similar frequency causes a series of regular peaks of intensity to be produced at the beat frequency, which is the difference between the signal frequencies.

Carrier: the high-frequency wave used to carry a low-frequency signal in A.M. or F.M. systems.

Catheter: the narrow plastic tube used to transmit fluid or fluid pressure from some point within the body.

Doppler shift: the apparent frequency shift of a sound source due to the relative movement between source and receiver.

Electrocardiogram: (E.C.G.) A record of the electrical activity of the heart.

Electroencephalogram: (E.E.G.) A record of the electrical activity of the brain.

Electromylogram: (E.M.G.) A record of the action potentials of muscle fibre.

Fidelity: a term used to describe quality of reproduction which depends on the bandwidth of a device.

Image lag: the image on a T.V. monitor is blurred if the response of the system is not sufficiently rapid to deal with the moving object; this response time is referred to as the image lag.

Impedance: the resistance of a device to A.C. formed from the resistive and reactive components within the device.

Input impedance: the open circuit impedance across the input terminals to a device.

Micron: 10^{-6} metres.

Manometer: a pressure measuring device.

Output impedance: the open circuit impedance across the output terminals to the device.

Picture: in T.V. systems the combination of two or more interlaced fields.

Polarisation: a collection of charge around an electrode.

Raster: the set of scanning lines across a field of a T.V. monitor.

Resistivity (ρ): is the term relating resistance R of a wire to its cross-sectional area, A and length, L by $R = \rho L/A$.

Resting potential: the potential difference across a semi-permeable membrane at equilibrium.

Transducer: a device which converts a signal from one form to another, e.g. a pressure signal into an electrical one.

THE COMPUTER

Process time: the time interval between calling and receiving data from a storage device.

Accumulator: the arithmetic unit of the computer in which arithmetical and logical operations are performed.

Address: a location in store which can be represented in a program by a name or number.

Analogue: the representation of a parameter by means of a physical variable.

Base: every number system has a base, which defines the power of the system, e.g. octal has the base 8 so that $17_8 = 15_{10}$.

Boolean algebra: a process of reasoning using symbolic logic to deal with operators such as AND, OR, NOT, etc. (named after George Boole 1815-1864).

Bit: a binary digit.

Character: a keyboard symbol.

Compiler: a program which converts a user's program into machine code commands.

Debug: to locate and remove mistakes from a program.

Digital: the representation of a physical variable by a number.

FORTRAN: FORmula TRANslation—a procedure oriented programming language.

Hardware: the electronics or electrical devices associated with a computer.

Integrated Circuit: a complete electronic circuit in which the various components are all part of the same piece of semiconductor.

Location: a position in core store which can hold one computer word and be identified by an address.

Loop: a sequence of commands which is repeated until a certain condition is satisfied.

Machine code: a programming language designed for the hardware of a particular computer.

Memory cycle: the time required to read and restore information from core store.

Off-line: referring to equipment not directly connected to the central processing unit of the computer.

On-line: referring to equipment directly connected to the central processing unit of the computer.

Program: a sequence of instructions for solving a problem on a computer.

Simulation: the representation of a physical system or phenomenon by a model on a computer or other system.

Software: programs and routines of a computer.

Terminal: an access point for a user to the computer usually by means of a teletype.

Word: the number of bits which can occupy a location in core store form a word; this is a definite number for a given computer.

Books Consulted

AUDIOLOGY
The Physics of the Ear, T. S. Littler, 1965. (Pergamon Press.)
A Review of Audiometry, D. W. Robinson, 1971. (*Phys. Med. Biol.* **16**, 1-24.)

COMPUTERS
Computer Science, P. Harvey, 1971. (Norman Price Limited.)
Electronic Computers Made Simple, H. Jacabowitz, 1967. (W. H. Allen.)
The Principles of Medical Computing, Thomas R. Taylor, 1967. (Blackwell.)

GENERAL
Applied Physiology 1961, Samson Wright's. (Oxford University Press.)
An Introduction to Human Physiology, J. H. Green, 1970. (Oxford University Press.)

RADIOLOGICAL PHYSICS
Anniversary Edition, British Journal of Radiology, August 1973.
Atomic and Nuclear Physics, T. A. Littlefield and N. Thorley, 1963. (Van Nostrand Co. Ltd.)
Fundamental Physics of Radiology, W. J. Meredith and J. B. Massey, 1968. (John Wright and Sons Limited.)
Instrumentation in Nuclear Medicine Volume I, Ed. G. J. Hine, 1967. (Academic Press.)
Radioisotopes in Medical Diagnosis, Ed. E. H. Belcher and H. Vetter, 1971. (Butterworths.)
Radiopharmaceuticals and Clinical Radiation Sources (*1973/74*), The Radiochemical Centre, Amersham.
A Short Textbook of Radiotherapy, J. Walter and H. Miller, 1969. (J. A. Churchill Ltd.)
X-Ray Physics and Equipment, F. Jaundrell-Thompson and W. J. Ashworth, 1965. (Blackwell Scientific Publications.)

PHYSIOLOGICAL MEASUREMENT
Biomedical Electronics, H. M. Yanof, 1972. (F. A. Davies Co.)
Electronic Measurement Techniques in Anaesthesia and Surgery, D. W. Hill, 1970. (Butterworths.)
I.E.E. Medical Electronics Monographs 1-6, Ed. B. W. Watson. (Peter Peregrins Limited.)
Principles of Electronics in Medical Research, D. W. Hill, 1965. (Butterworths.)

ULTRASONICS
Ultrasonics in Clinical Diagnosis, Ed. P. N. T. Wells, 1972. (Churchill Livingstone.)

INDEX